The Wizard of Oz

Illustrated by Dania Florino

Retold by Joshua George

Licensed exclusively to Top That Publishing Ltd
Tide Mill Way, Woodbridge, Suffolk, IP12 1AP, UK
www.topthatpublishing.com
Copyright © 2014 Tide Mill Media
All rights reserved
0 2 4 6 8 9 7 5 3 1
Printed and bound in China

ISBN 978-1-78244-672-9

A catalogue record for this book is available from the British Library

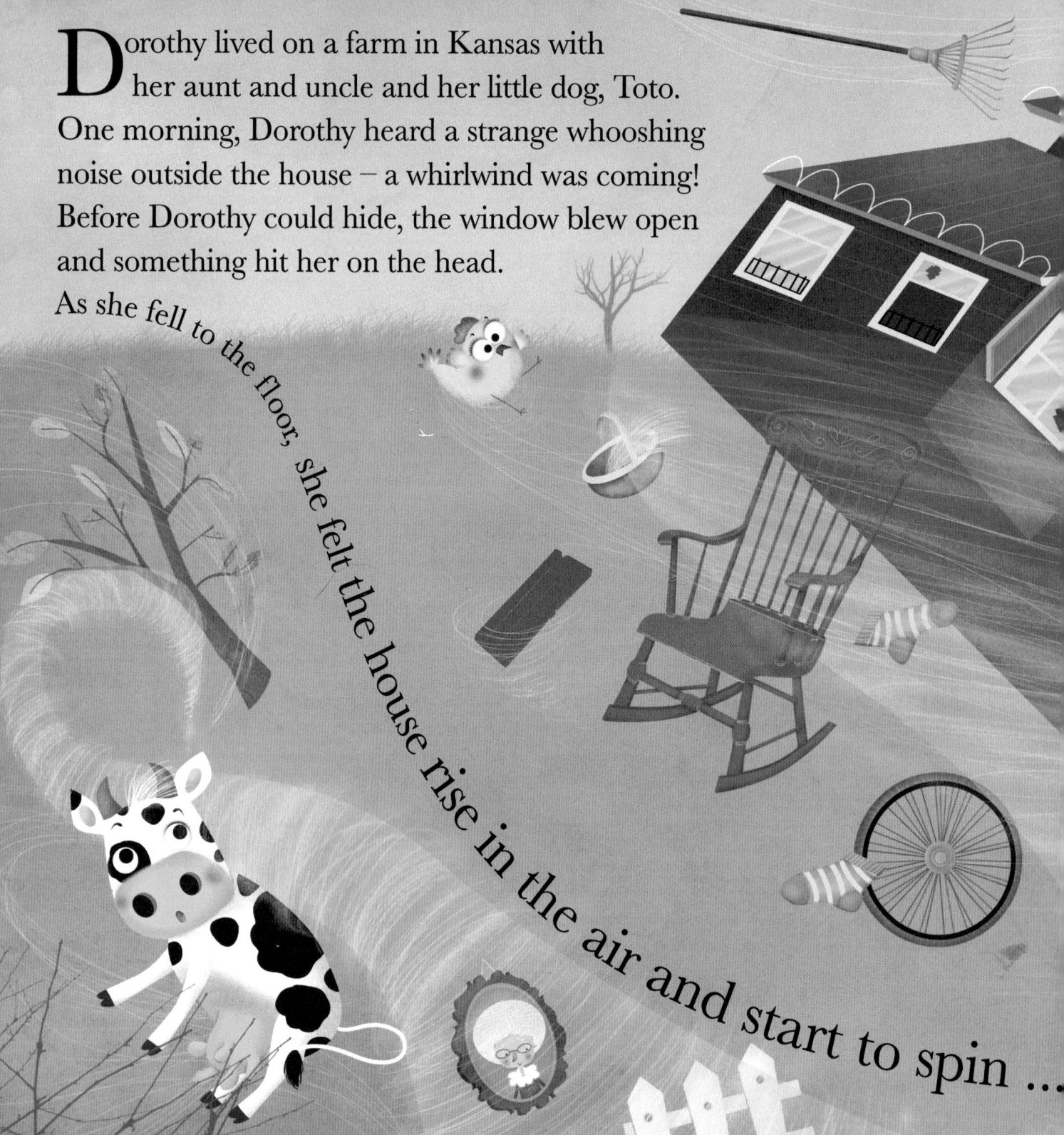

Dorothy lived on a farm in Kansas with her aunt and uncle and her little dog, Toto. One morning, Dorothy heard a strange whooshing noise outside the house — a whirlwind was coming! Before Dorothy could hide, the window blew open and something hit her on the head.

As she fell to the floor, she felt the house rise in the air and start to spin ...

around and around and around and around!

When Dorothy woke up, the wind had stopped and the house was still. Cautiously, she opened the door.

'Goodness!' she exclaimed.

'This doesn't look like Kansas!'

Then Dorothy spotted a crowd of people.

'Thank you for saving us from the Wicked Witch of the East!'

cried the crowd, happily.

And there, sticking out from under the house, were two feet wearing red shoes.

Dorothy had landed on the Witch!

'Don't worry, dear,' said a tall lady. 'You're in the land of Oz, and I'm Glinda, the Good Witch.'

'But how do I get home to Kansas?' asked Dorothy.

'The Wizard of Oz can help,' replied Glinda. 'Take the Wicked Witch of the East's magic shoes and follow the yellow brick road to the Emerald City. You'll find him there.'

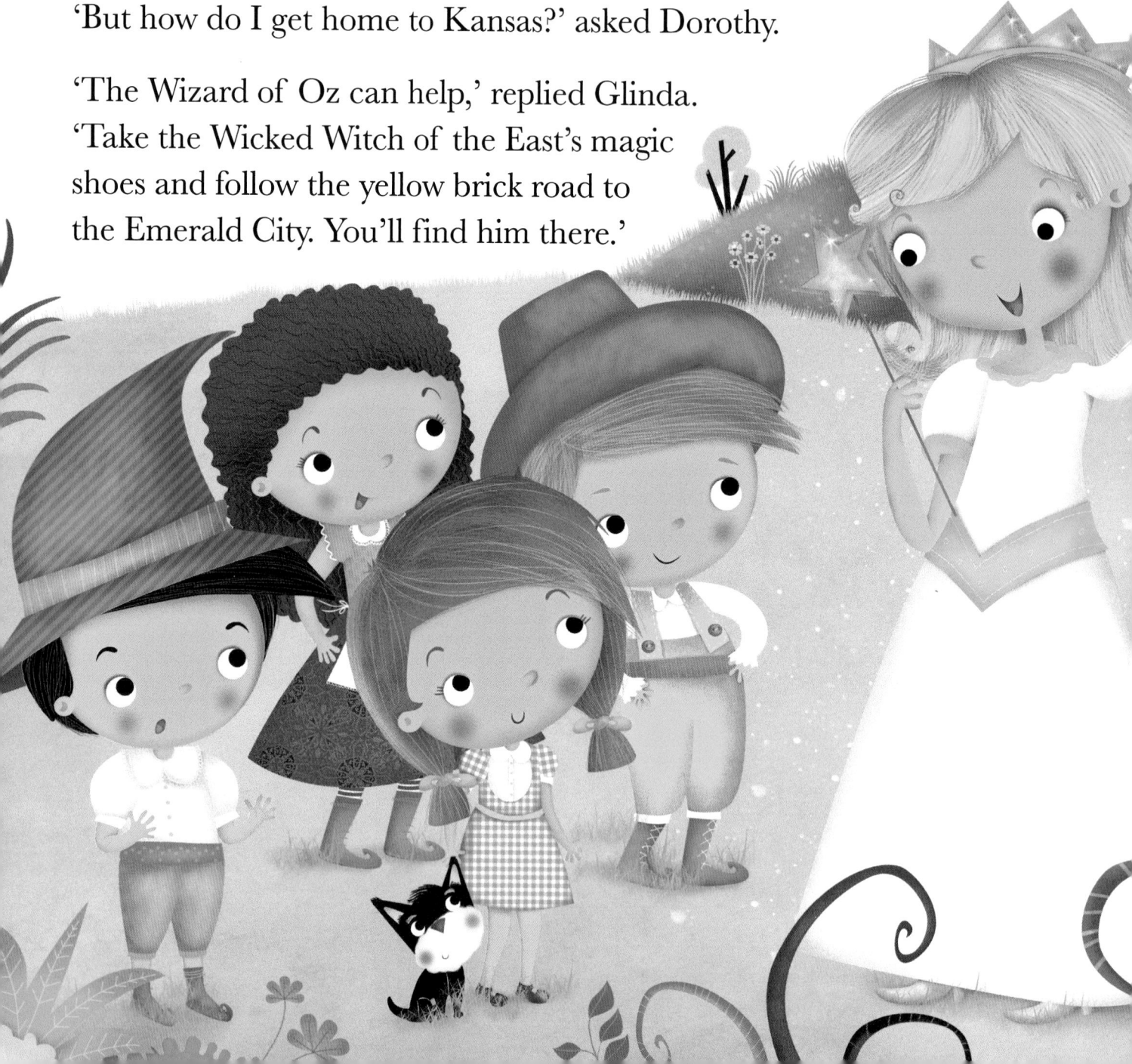

Nearby, the Wicked Witch of the West was hiding. She was angry because Dorothy had landed on her sister and was even wearing her magic shoes!

'I want those shoes,' she hissed.

Dorothy and Toto set off along the yellow brick road. As they passed a field, Dorothy was amazed to see a scarecrow wink and wave at her!

Dorothy stopped and chatted to the scarecrow, telling him all about her journey to the Emerald City.

'Maybe the Wizard could give me some brains!' said the Scarecrow hopefully.

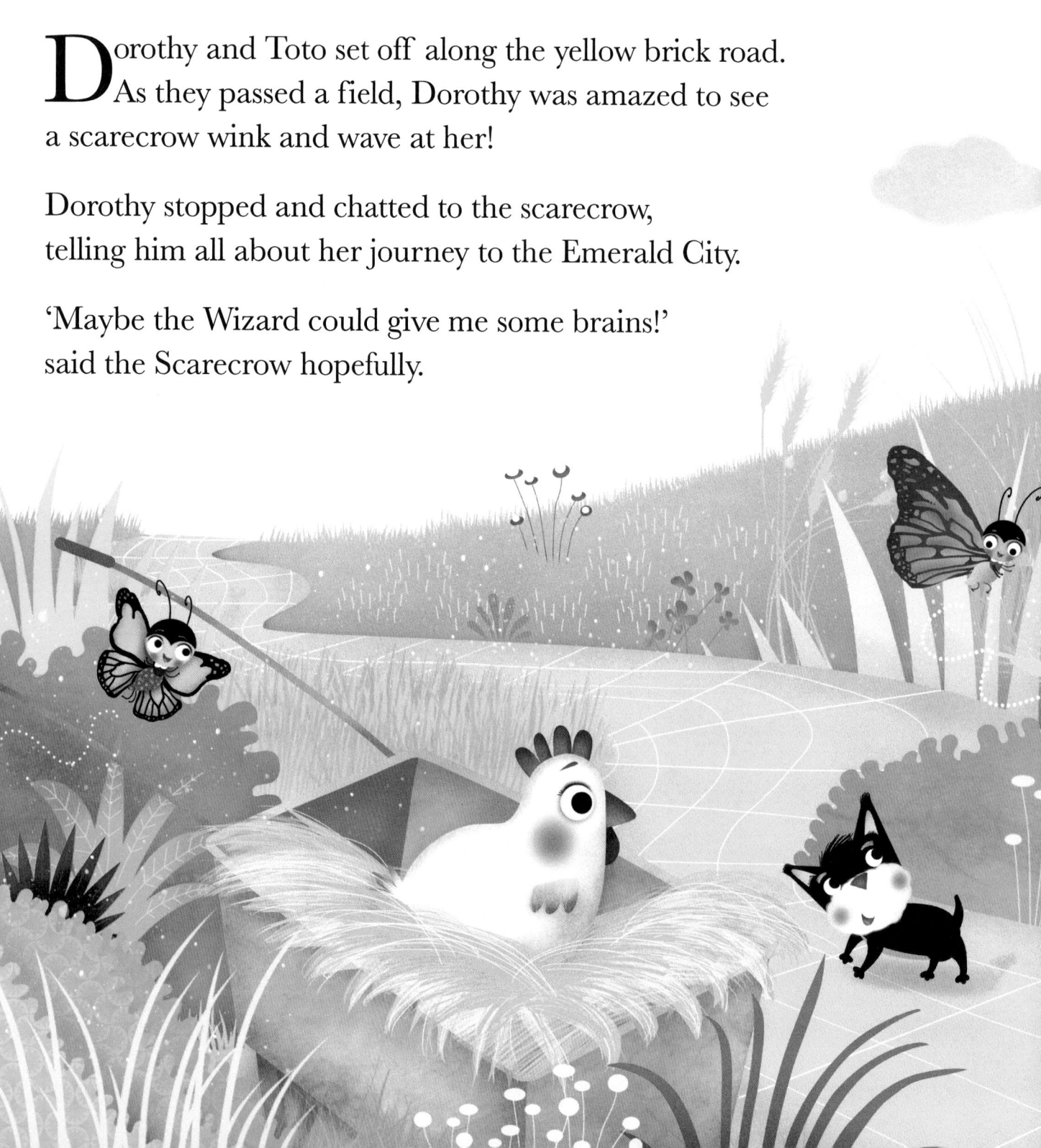

'Then why don't you come too?'
asked Dorothy, and they set off together.

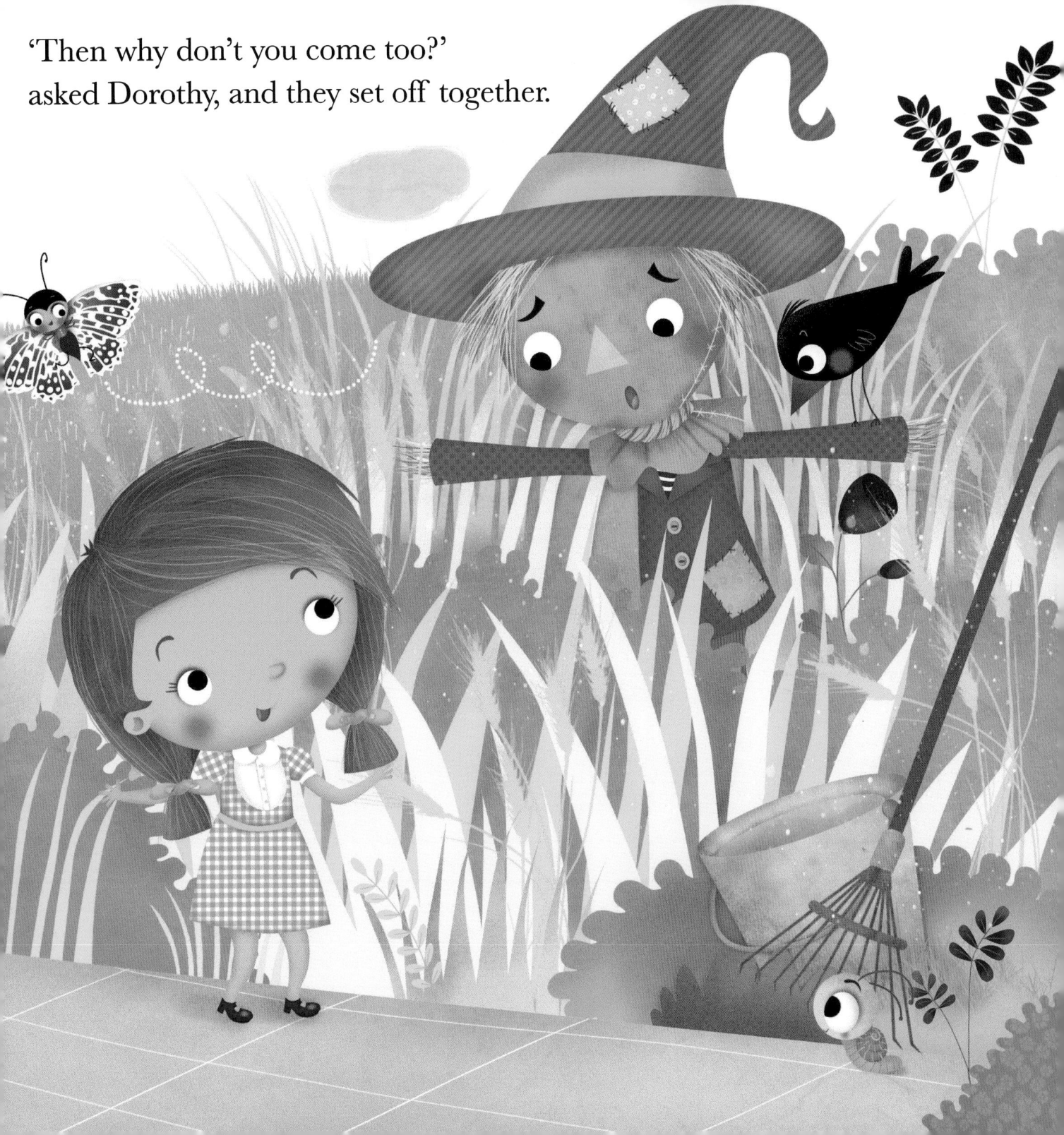

Soon, Dorothy, Toto and the Scarecrow met a man made of tin, who squeaked with every step.

'I'll help you oil those creaky joints,' Dorothy said, kindly, telling him about their journey as she did so.

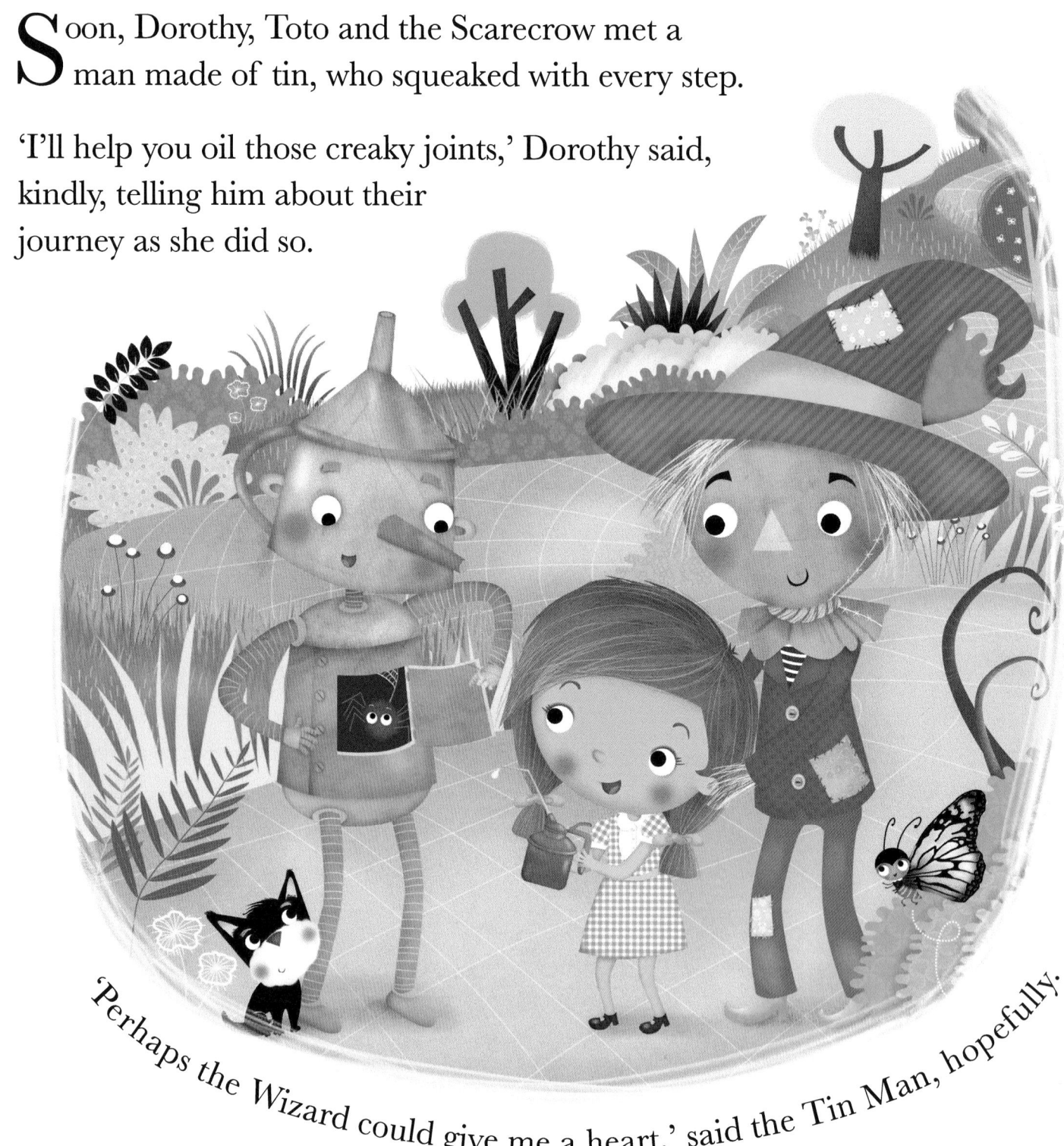

'Perhaps the Wizard could give me a heart,' said the Tin Man, hopefully.

Later that day, a lion bounded out of the woods
and Toto barked at him, bravely.

'Boo hoo,' cried the Lion. 'I'm supposed to be
King of the Animals, but I don't have any courage.'

'Come with us to see the Wizard,' suggested Dorothy, so he did!

After a very long walk, the friends spotted the green glow of the Emerald City.

'Look!' exclaimed Dorothy as they got closer. 'Everything is green ... even the people!'

The friends went to see the Wizard straight away.

'I'll help you all if you bring me the Wicked Witch of the West's broomstick,' he said.

'We'll have to do it,' said the Lion, 'or I'll never get my courage.'
'Or my brains!' said the Scarecrow.
'Or my heart!' said the Tin Man.

'And I'll never get back to Kansas!' cried Dorothy.

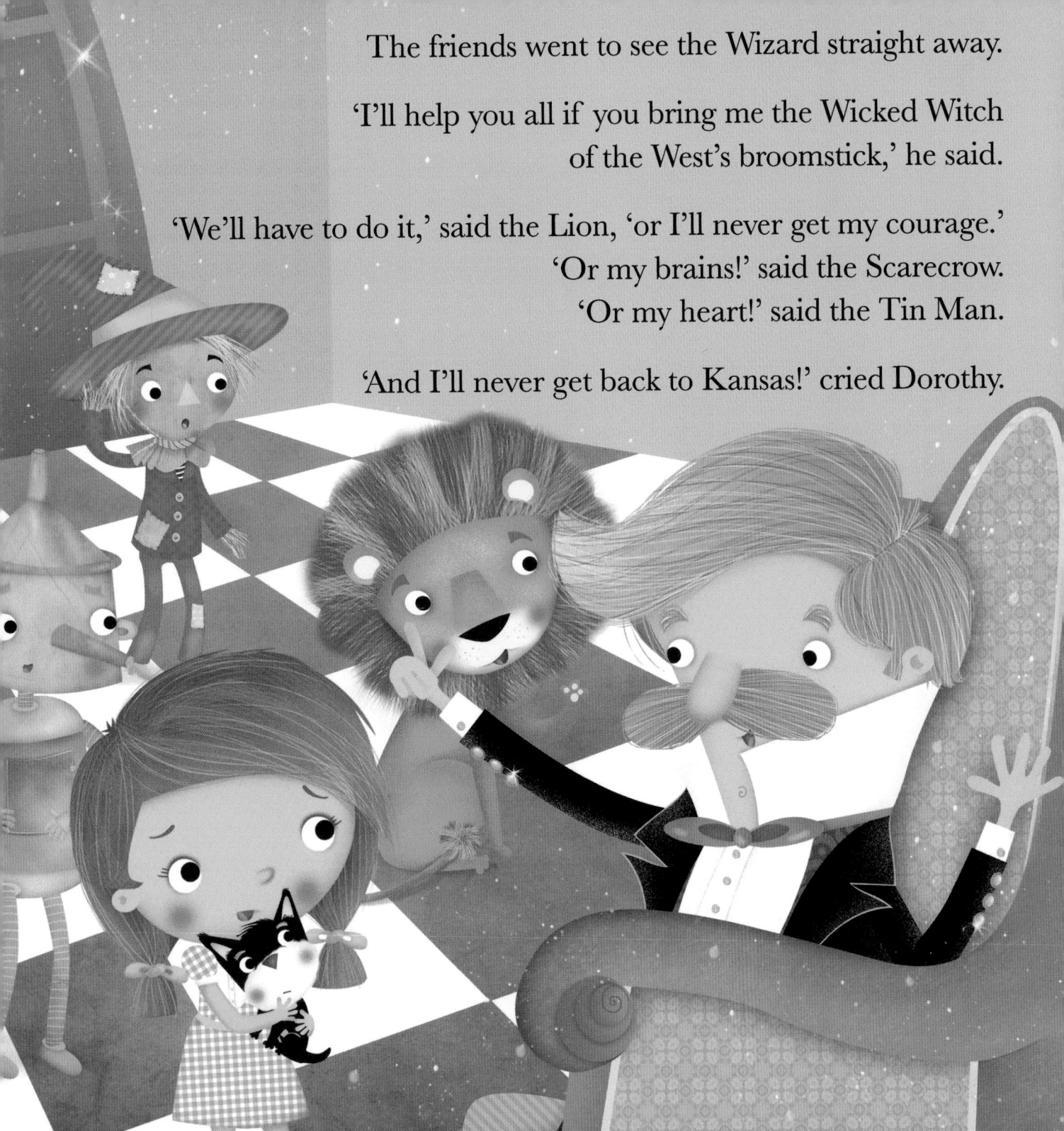

So the friends set off towards the Wicked Witch's castle in the West.

They crossed mountains full of lurking wolves …

and tiptoed through forests full of scary bees and glowing eyes!

But the Wicked Witch found out that they were coming and sent a troop of flying monkeys to stop them!

The Lion roared! The Tin Man swung his axe!
And even the Scarecrow tried to fight!
But the monkeys grabbed Dorothy and Toto and
dragged them to the Wicked Witch's castle.

'**Ha-ha-HA!**' cackled the Wicked Witch. '**Now the magic shoes are mine!**'

The Wicked Witch was so excited about the shoes that she didn't notice Toto creep away to find the others to help Dorothy escape. Soon, the friends had sneaked into the castle and freed Dorothy.

When the Witch saw what was happening,
she shot sparks at the Scarecrow who burst into flames!

Quickly, Dorothy threw a bucket
of water over her friend.

'Eeek!'

she squealed in surprise,
as some water splashed
the Witch and turned her
into a giant puddle!

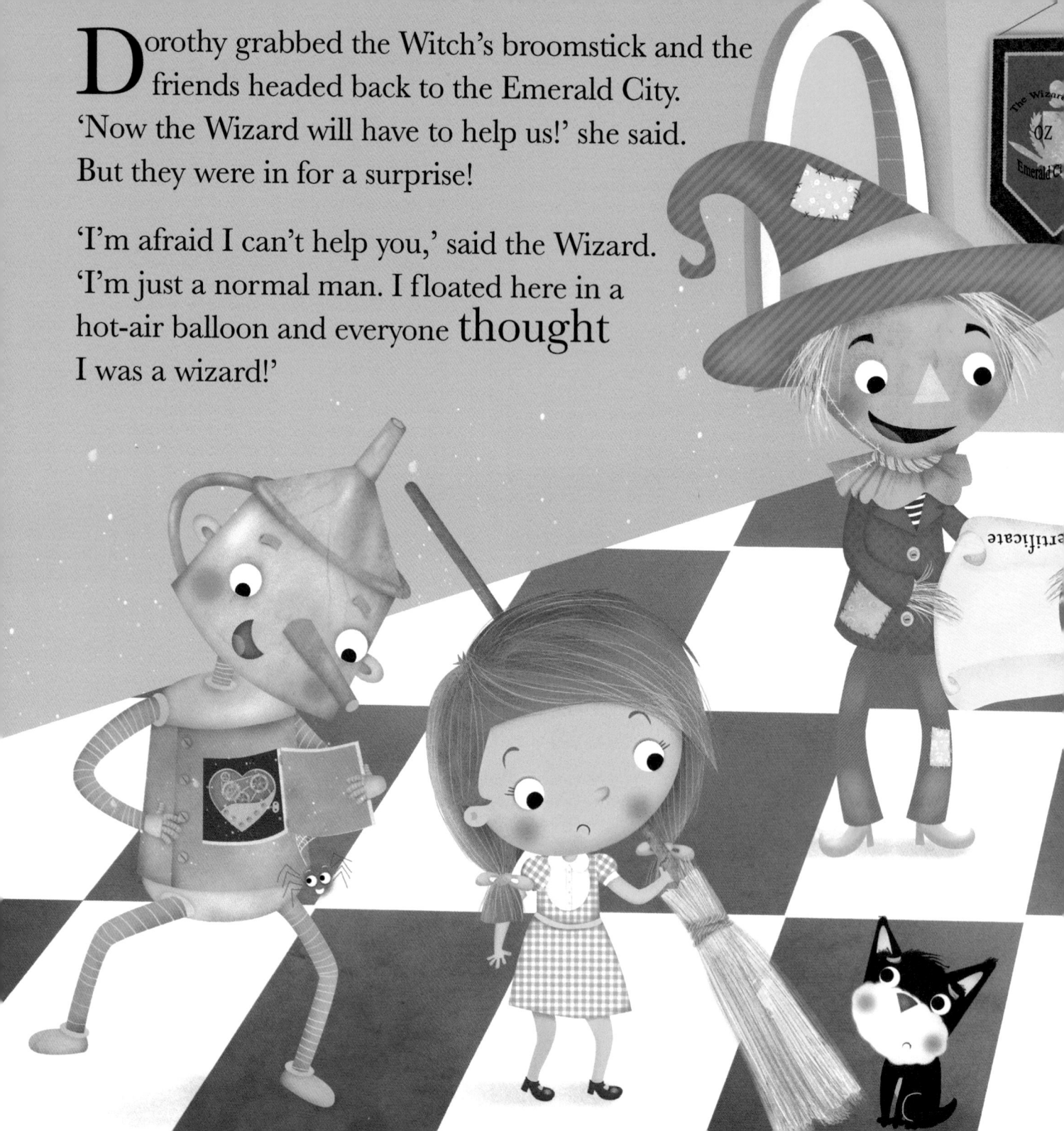

Dorothy grabbed the Witch's broomstick and the friends headed back to the Emerald City. 'Now the Wizard will have to help us!' she said. But they were in for a surprise!

'I'm afraid I can't help you,' said the Wizard. 'I'm just a normal man. I floated here in a hot-air balloon and everyone **thought** I was a wizard!'

Dorothy started to cry, and so did the Scarecrow, the Tin Man and the Lion.

'But I can give you these,' said the Wizard, handing the Scarecrow a certificate, the Tin Man a clockwork heart and the Lion a big medal for bravery.

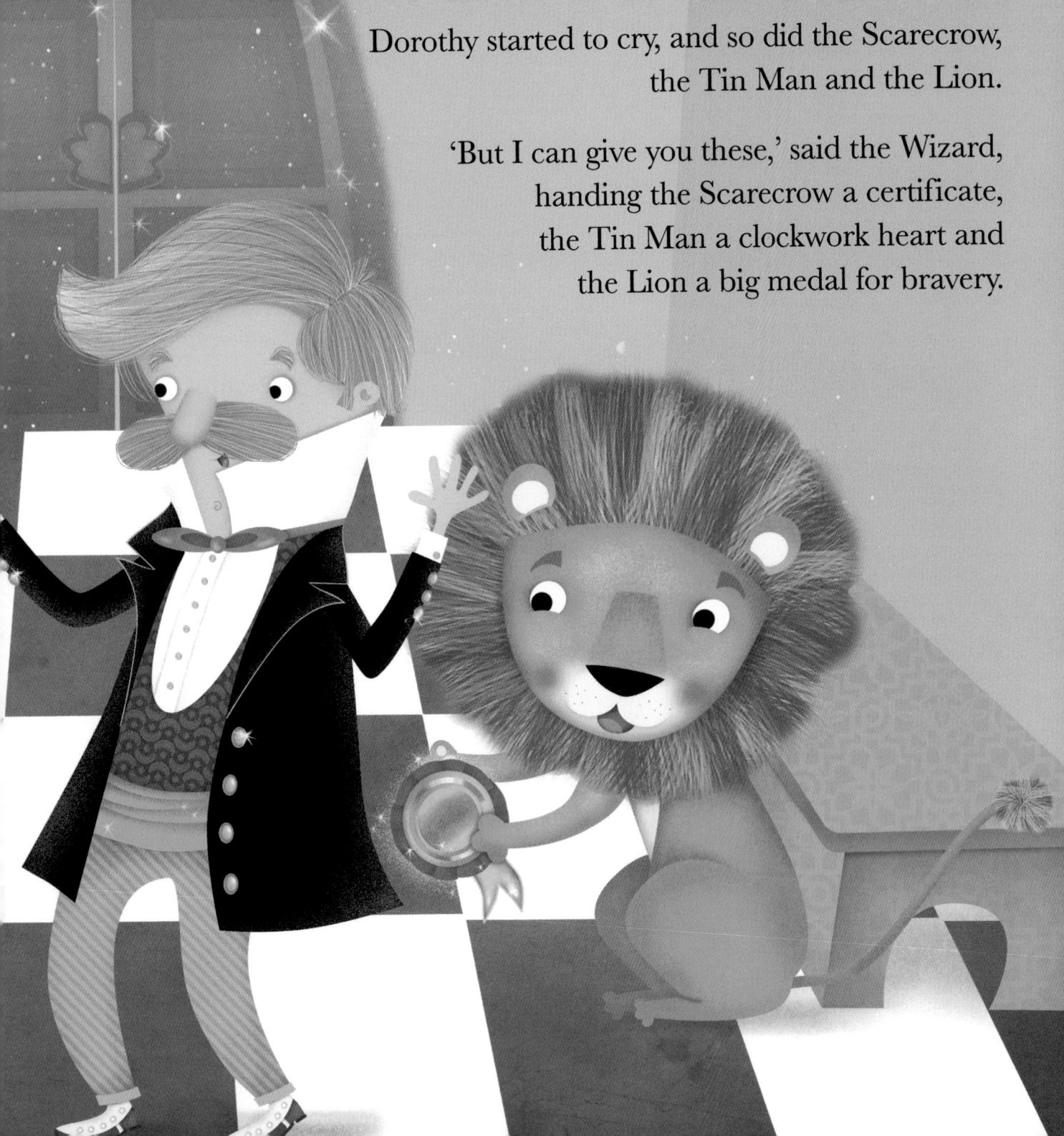

'What about me?' said Dorothy, sadly.

'Don't worry,' said the Wizard.
'I'll take you home in my hot-air balloon!'

But just as they were about to take off,
Toto jumped out of the basket and ran off!

'Wait!' yelled Dorothy,
leaping out after him.

'I'm sorry,' said the Wizard, as the balloon

floated away. 'I can't stop it!'

Dorothy started to cry.

'How will I ever get home?' she sobbed.

Then, with a puff of smoke and a shower of rainbow-coloured sparkles, another witch appeared.

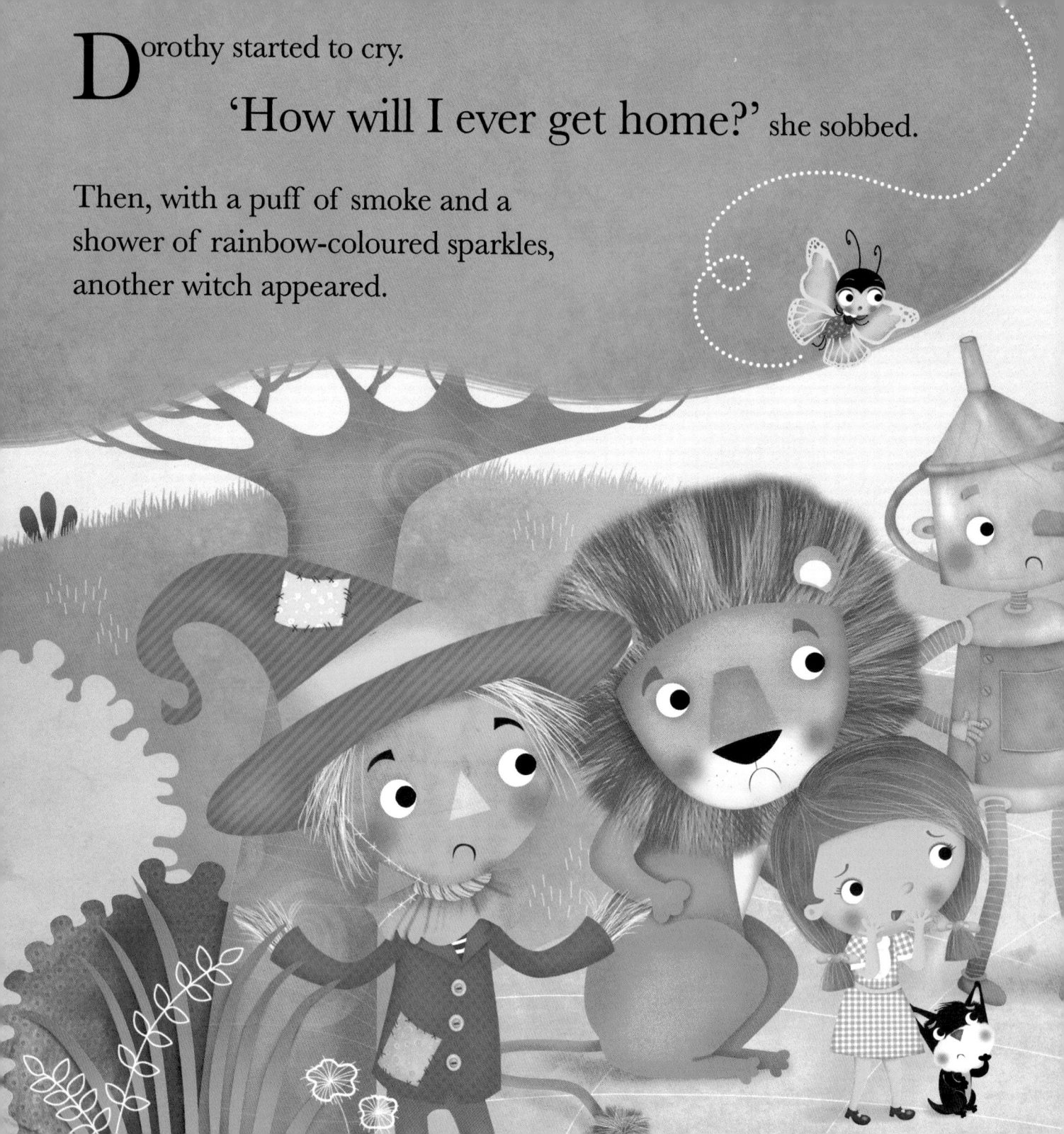

'Don't cry,' she said. 'I'm the Good Witch of the South. You've helped your friends, so I'm going to help YOU! Just click your heels together three times, say, "There's no place like home," and you'll see!'

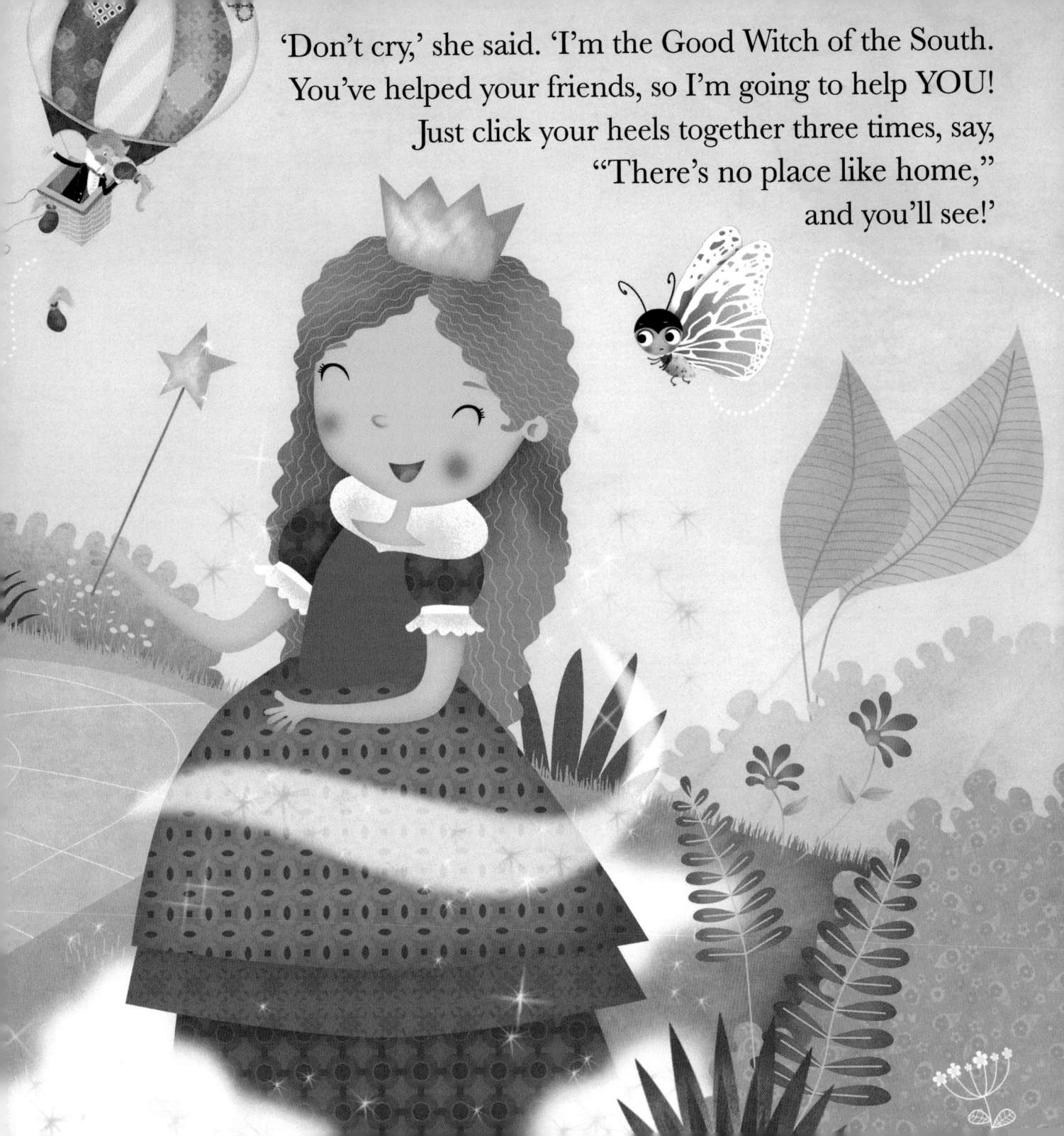

So Dorothy said goodbye to her friends.

'I'll miss you all so much,' she said.
Then, holding Toto tightly, she clicked
her heels three times and said,

'There's no place like home.'

Suddenly, she was back in Kansas!
There was her house – and her aunt and uncle.

'What an adventure!' she thought.
'But the Good Witch was right.
There really is no place like home!'

Printed in Great Britain
by Amazon

CAPE TOWN & THE WINELANDS' TOP 10

➓ Cape Town & the Winelands' Highlights

Modern visitors would agree with Sir Francis Drake's testament to the Cape region as "the fairest Cape in the whole circumference of the earth". Cape Town, sandwiched between the imperious heights of Table Mountain and the blue depths of the Atlantic, has a sensational setting. With its Mediterranean climate, the city is a haven for outdoor enthusiasts, offering hiking opportunities along the spine of the Cape Peninsula, local wildlife to glimpse, lush winelands to explore and pristine beaches on which to relax. For visitors inclined towards cultural pursuits, Cape Town has a vibrant Afro-fusion cultural scene, a rich sense of history and eye-catching colonial architecture.

The Company's Garden 1
Overshadowed by majestic Table Mountain, this park was established by the first Dutch settlers in 1652 and features an eclectic mix of museums and galleries (see pp8–9).

Milnerto
Cape Town
see map below
Clifton Bay
Pinelan
Table Mountain 5
M3
Kirstenbos
National 6
Botanical
Garden
Constantia
Groot Constantia 7
Wine Estate
Berg
Chapman's
Point
Muizenberg
Noordhoek
Kommetjie
Fish Ho
Glencairn
Simon's Town 8
Cape
Peninsula
National
Park
Cape of 9
Good Hope

The V&A Waterfront
2 Outdoor cafés, a vibrant nightlife and exciting shopping can be enjoyed at this waterfront complex. It is also the departure point for trips to Robben Island (see pp10–11).

District Six Museum 3
This stirring Cape Town museum documents the apartheid-era evictions of "non-whites" from the central suburb of District Six to the remote Cape Flats (see pp14–15).

Castle of Good Hope
4 Constructed in the 1670s, South Africa's oldest extant building now houses several museums. The ramparts of the castle overlook the Grand Parade, where rapturous crowds gathered to greet Nelson Mandela on his release from jail in 1990 (see pp16–17).

➤ Preceding pages **The V&A Waterfront**

5 Table Mountain

The thrilling aerial ascent of magnificent Table Mountain leads to a succession of stunning views over the Cape Peninsula and the Winelands (*see pp18–19*).

6 Kirstenbosch National Botanical Garden

At its best during the spring wildflower season, this garden protects the floral wealth of the Western Cape and is a year-round visitor attraction (*see pp20–21*).

7 Groot Constantia Wine Estate

South Africa's oldest estate, Groot Constantia is noted for its old-world Cape Dutch architecture nestled amongst leafy vineyards (*see pp22–3*).

8 Simon's Town and Boulders Beach

All quaint Victorian façades overlooking the splendid False Bay, this sleepy naval town is famed for the comical colony of penguins that waddles around on nearby Boulders Beach. (*see pp24–5*).

10 Stellenbosch

Despite its wealth of impressive Cape Dutch architecture, South Africa's second-oldest town is better known – and justifiably so – as the most central base for exploring the renowned Cape Winelands (*see pp28–9*).

9 Cape of Good Hope Nature Reserve

Pink-hued proteas, grazing antelope and mischievous baboons can be observed at the peninsula's southern tip, where a clifftop lighthouse offers bird's-eye views over Cape Point (*see pp26–7*).

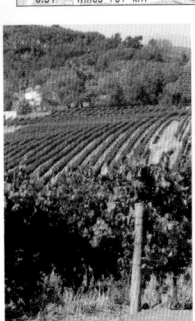

📻10 The Company's Garden

This blissful oasis of shade and greenery at the heart of Cape Town is surrounded by the city's most important concentration of old buildings and museums. It was established by Jan van Riebeeck in 1652, just weeks after his arrival at the Cape, to provide fresh produce to passing Dutch ships. By the 18th century, what was created as a vegetable patch had transformed into a world-renowned botanical garden that spread over 18 hectares (44 acres) and exported bulbs and other produce to Europe. Today, the garden is a popular lunchtime retreat for city workers. The park-like lawns are inhabited by flocks of feral pigeons and tame squirrels and offer stunning views of the ragged cliffs of Table Mountain.

Walkway, Rose Garden

🌀 Some museums are closed on Sundays. The National Gallery and SA Museum are free on Saturdays.

🍵 Try the Gardens Tea Room opposite the aviary.

• Map P5 • Entrance Orange, Queen Victoria, Adderley, Wale and Hatfield Sts
• (021) 422 5956
• Garden: open 7am–7pm daily; free
• Museum & Planetarium: open 10am–5pm daily; museum adm R20 (adults), R6 (kids); planetarium adm R20 (adults), R6 (kids) • Slave Lodge: open 10am–5pm Mon–Sat; adm R15 (adults), R5 (students and pensioners)
• National Gallery: open 10am–5pm Tue–Sun; adm R15 (adults), R5 (students), free under-16yrs
www.iziko.org.za

Top 10 Features

1. Iziko Slave Lodge
2. St George's Cathedral
3. Entrance to Old Company's Garden
4. Rhodes Statue
5. Aviary & Slave Bell
6. Tree Grove
7. Rose Garden
8. Delville Wood Memorial
9. Iziko South African Museum & Iziko Planetarium
10. South African National Gallery

Iziko Slave Lodge

Founded in 1679, this handsome building *(right)*, once an unsanitary and cramped slaves' home, is now a museum charting the history of slave trade.

St George's Cathedral

This Anglican cathedral *(above)* was a centre of political protest during the 1980s, and the site of clashes between the police and protesters. The oldest part of the building is a crypt designed by Sir Herbert Baker.

Entrance to Old Company's Garden

Flanked by the Slave Lodge and St George's Cathedral, the garden's main entrance *(below)* has not changed position since the 1670s.

Rhodes Statue
Commissioned in 1908, this statue of CJ Rhodes *(left)* depicts the politician with his right arm raised northwards, symbolizing his aim to make Africa a British colony.

Aviary & Slave Bell
The aviary opposite the Gardens Tea Room houses parrots, while the Slave Bell is a fire bell that was moved from Greenmarket Square.

Tree Grove
Some of the garden's oldest trees grow in this enclave, including a tree aloe and other forest perennials.

Rose Garden
The garden was the site of the Cape's first wine-producing vine and a source of rosewater in the Dutch era. A central memorial is dedicated to HIV/AIDS victims.

Delville Wood Memorial
Featuring sculptures by Anton van Wouw and Alfred Turner, this stark memorial *(above)* unveiled in 1930 commemorates the South African casualties of World War I in Delville Wood, France.

Archbishop Desmond Tutu

Desmond Tutu, the first black Archbishop of Cape Town was the bishop of St George's Cathedral. During his tenure, the church was an important centre of the anti-apartheid movement. Post apartheid, this 1984 Nobel Peace Prize winner chaired the Truth and Reconciliation Commission, and now addresses HIV/AIDS issues.

Iziko South African Museum & Planetarium
To the garden's south, this 19th-century mansion *(left)* houses natural history displays, rock art and prehistoric artifacts. Beside it stands the large-domed planetarium.

South African National Gallery
From an initial bequest of 45 paintings in 1871, the gallery is now the sub-Saharan region's leading art museum. Apart from its African and European collections, it also features temporary exhibitions.

 The planetarium's shows on southern hemisphere constellations are at 2pm Mon–Fri (also 8pm Tue); noon, 1pm & 2:30pm Sat–Sun.

TOP10 The V&A Waterfront

There may well be larger shopping complexes than the V&A (Victoria & Alfred) Waterfront, but none boasts as scenic a location. Sandwiched between the sparkling waters of the Atlantic and the majestic contours of Table Mountain (centre), the waterfront is emblematic of Cape Town's resurgence in the post-apartheid era, and is integral to the modern-day city. The Waterfront complex opened in 1992 and has played an important role in reversing the economic decline that had gripped the historic docklands since the 1960s. Also a functional harbour to this day, the V&A Waterfront is ranked as South Africa's most-visited tourist attraction, with a huge choice of eateries, hundreds of shops, numerous sights and several leisure activities, including day tours to Robben Island.

Two Oceans Aquarium

Don't miss the sensational views of Table Mountain. Look out, too, for the seals and gulls that make the harbour their home.

There are several restaurants and cafés to choose from *(see p68).*

- Map P2–Q2
- (021) 408 7600
- Connected by regular buses to the city centre and Sea Point
- Shops: open 9am–9pm Mon–Sun & public hols
- www.waterfront.co.za
- Two Oceans Aquarium: Dock Rd; (021) 418 3823; open 9:30am–6pm daily; adm R88 (adults), R42 (kids), R68 (students & pensioners), free under-4 yrs; www.aquarium.co.za

Top 10 Features

1. Two Oceans Aquarium
2. Craft Market & Wellness Centre
3. Nobel Square
4. Swing Bridge & Clock Tower
5. Nelson Mandela Gateway
6. Alfred Mall
7. African Trading Post
8. Victoria Wharf Shopping Mall
9. Vaughan Johnson's Wine & Cigar Shop
10. Bay & Sunset Cruise

1 Two Oceans Aquarium

Over 3,000 marine creatures are housed here. Popular exhibits include the "River Meander" with its tame penguins and oyster-catchers, and a kelp forest with fish *(below).*

2 Craft Market & Wellness Centre

More than 120 stalls in South Africa's largest indoor craft market offer everything from African beadwork to tarot readings and holistic health treatments.

3 Nobel Square

Life-sized statues of four Nobel Peace Prize winners – Luthuli, Tutu, de Klerk and Mandela *(below)* – are set alongside Noria Mabasa's intriguing Makonde-esque sculpture.

The Two Oceans Aquarium allows visitors to dive into shark tanks for an additional fee; R380 if own equipment, R485 to rent.

Swing Bridge & Clock Tower

A piece of Victoriana, the iconic Clock Tower dates back to 1882. It is reached via a swing bridge that opens to accommodate passing boats *(above)*.

Nelson Mandela Gateway

This is the embarkation point for day tours to Robben Island. It also houses multimedia displays documenting the island's history.

Alfred Mall

Lined with alfresco bars and cafés, this converted Edwardian warehouse *(left)* is an excellent spot to down refreshments while soaking up the idyllic views over the harbour to Table Mountain.

African Trading Post

Shelves of local music CDs and T-shirts are stocked alongside handcrafted beadwork and authentic Africana items at this craft and curio shop *(above)*.

Vaughan Johnson's Wine & Cigar Shop

Whether it is vintage award-winners or the shop's affordable own-label products, this wine shop *(above)* is the place to stock up on a few bottles.

Victoria Wharf Shopping Mall

Recuperate from shopping at one of the many restaurants, then catch a movie at the Art Nouveau or Nu Metro cinemas – all in one of South Africa's largest malls.

Bay & Sunset Cruise

You can take a sunset cruise around Table Bay with one of the operators who can be found on Quay 5 and North Wharf.

History of the Docklands

The docklands started to take shape in the 19th century, when in 1860, Prince Alfred (son of Queen Victoria) began the construction of the Alfred Basin by tipping a load of stones into the sea. Despite extensive development over the years, several Victorian buildings on the Waterfront, such as the Ferryman and Mitchell's Pubs and Breakwater Lodge, are still standing.

⑩ Robben Island

Situated in Table Bay, Robben Island is South Africa's answer to Alcatraz and has been a place of exile since Van Riebeeck's day. Its first political prisoner, a rebellious local trader named Autshumatom, was sent here in 1658. By the 1760s, the island held 70 prisoners, including several Muslim leaders. Today, it is best known for its role under apartheid, when Robert Sobukwe, Nelson Mandela, Walter Sisulu, Govan Mbeki (father of Thabo Mbeki) and Jacob Zuma among others were imprisoned here. The last prisoner left in 1996 and the island is now a museum.

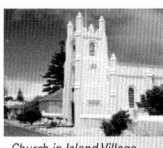

Church in Island Village

🚩 Arrive at Nelson Mandela Gateway at least 30 minutes prior to departure to explore its museum.

🍴 There's nowhere to eat or drink on the island, but cafés are scattered around the departure point at the V&A Waterfront.

• Map A2
• (021) 405 4500
• Departures from the Nelson Mandela Gateway on the Waterfront: 9am, 11am, 1pm, 3pm weather permitting; guided tours with return ferry ride: 3½– 4 hours • Adm R180 (adults), R90 (kids); book online • www. robben-island.org.za

Top 10 Features

1. Ferry Trip
2. Robben Island Village
3. Murray Bay
4. Kramat of Tuan Guru
5. Jan van Riebeeck Quarry
6. Leper's Graveyard
7. Robert Sobukwe's House
8. Lighthouse
9. Limestone Quarry
10. Maximum Security Prison

Ferry Trip
1 The 30-minute ferry trip *(above)* from the V&A Waterfront is best on calm clear days, with fabulous views across Table Bay. Keep a look out for dolphins and seals.

Robben Island Village
2 Formerly home to the prison wardens, this small village consists of residential quarters for the museum staff. It also has two old churches, one built from sandstone in 1895, and the other a garrison-like construction dating back to 1841.

Murray Bay
3 Robben Island's small harbour is home to 140,000 African penguins *(left)*, making it the third largest colony in South Africa. Rather incongruously, the penguins are often seen in the company of the island's ubiquitous feral rabbits.

 Robben Island was named after the colony of seals that inhabited the island in the 17th century – robben is Dutch for "seal".

Kramat of Tuan Guru

The island bus-tour's first stop is the shrine to Tuan Guru *(above)*, an Indonesian Islamic cleric jailed here by the Dutch in the 18th century.

Jan van Riebeeck Quarry

The blue slate used to build the Castle of Good Hope was quarried by Van Riebeeck at the far south of the island. Bontebok and eland are often seen here.

Leper's Graveyard

This cemetery *(above)* seen from the bus tour is testament to the island's role as a leper colony from 1846 to 1930.

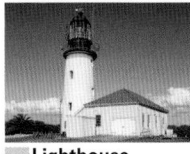

Lighthouse

The lighthouse *(above)* was built in 1865 on Minto Hill, the island's highest point. It replaced the fire beacons that were once in use.

Robert Sobukwe's House

Possibly the island's most forlorn sight, this is the house where PAC's Robert Sobukwe was held in confinement.

Maximum Security Prison

Conducted by former prisoners, the tour of the maximum security block is the sombre highlight of a visit to Robben Island. It includes a peek into Mandela's tiny cell *(left)* and incorporates photographic mementos of that era.

Limestone Quarry

Mandela undertook hard labour here. At a reunion in 1990, former prisoners spontaneously laid a cairn at this site.

Nelson Mandela

Mandela, born in 1918, was the first member of his family to attend school. His political career began in 1944 when, along with Oliver Tambo and Walter Sisulu, he formed the ANC Youth League. Mandela was accused of high treason in 1956, but charges against him were dropped after a four-year trial. However, he was captured and incarcerated on Robben Island in 1964 under charges of treason. Released from jail in 1990, he went on to win the Nobel Peace Prize in 1993 and became president of South Africa in 1994. He stepped down in 1999.

10 District Six Museum

Founded in 1994, this award-winning, community-funded museum draws on a rich repository of possession, photographs and recollections supplied by the forcibly dispossessed residents of District Six. A prosaically named municipal district, District Six was re-zoned as a whites-only area under the Group Areas Act during the apartheid era (see p34). The museum's exhibits celebrate everyday life as it was in this once-vibrant multiracial suburb, and mourn the destruction that it was subjected to at the hands of the apartheid government. Possibly the most moving of Cape Town's many museums, the District Six Museum provides some insight into the insidious effects of the racial discrimination propagated by the government on the day-to-day life of the ordinary folk who were victimized by it.

Museum façade

🎫 Many township tours start with a quick peek into the District Six Museum, but it is also worth visiting independently to absorb the minutiae of its detailed and poignant displays.

🍴 A coffee shop at the back sells cheap snacks such as sandwiches and pies. Several nearby restaurants serve more filling fare, including the coffee shop in the Castle of Good Hope (see p16).

- Map Q5
- 25A Buitenkant St
- (021) 466 7200
- Open 9am–3pm Mon, 9am–4pm Tue–Sat, Sun by appt
- Adm R15 (adults), R5 (kids)
- For tours, bk in adv
- www.districtsix.co.za

Top 10 Features

1 Painted Floor Map
2 Methodist Church Building
3 "Formation, Resistance, Restitution" Wall Panels
4 Nomvuyo's Room
5 Story of Horstley Street
6 Tribute to Langarm Pioneers
7 Barbershop Display
8 Bloemhof Flats Display
9 Sound Domes
10 Little Wonder Bookshop

Painted Floor Map
In the main hall, a hand-painted street map of District Six in its heyday is annotated by former residents with the locations of their houses before the bulldozers arrived (centre).

Methodist Church Building
The museum is housed in the Buitenkant Methodist Church, a former wine shop that was sanctified in 1883. The church was forcibly shut down for its stance against apartheid.

"Formation, Resistance, Restitution" Wall Panels
Using a combination of pictures, hard facts and interviews with former residents, this series of three wall panels (below) recounts the history of District Six since its creation in 1867.

Nomvuyo's Room

This simple exhibit *(below)* re-creates the single multi-purpose room that served as the family home of South African author Nomvuyo Ngcelwane, her parents and three siblings, prior to their forced eviction.

Story of Horstley Street

The memorial hall charts the history of Horstley Street. The mosaic and concrete floor *(above)* has written recollections of residents.

Key

Ground floor

First floor

Tribute to Langarm Pioneers

Grainy photographs, period recordings and a stack of 78s by Swing musicians such as the Heartthrobs, form a tantalizing introduction to the distinctively South African Langarm "jazz" that rocked District Six during the 1930s–50s.

Barbershop Display

This cheerfully nostalgic exhibit is a reconstruction of a typical 1950s barbershop, complete with period advertising plates pinned to the wall.

Bloemhof Flats Display

These poignant displays show photographs of Bloemhof Flats, a multiple-block housing development that was built over slummy Wells Square, and was famed for its football team.

Sound Domes

Place your shoes on the marked footprint in front of the mural on the inside front wall of the first floor, and listen to a sequence of ten different stories narrated by former residents of District Six.

Little Wonder Bookshop

It might be small, but this bookshop *(right)* on the ground floor stocks a comprehensive selection of titles about District Six and the many other forced mass evictions undertaken by the apartheid regime.

The Destruction of District Six

Cape Town's sixth municipal district was established in 1867 on the slopes below Devil's Peak. Its residents comprised freed slaves, immigrants and people of mixed race – the so-called Coloureds. The forced removal of Black residents by the police started in 1901; by 1967, 60,000 residents had been removed to the Cape Flats. The first to return post-apartheid were handed their house keys by Mandela.

 Share your travel recommendations on traveldk.com

TOP 10 Castle of Good Hope

Constructed between 1666 and 1679, the imposing Castle of Good Hope is the oldest functional building in South Africa. Pentagonal in shape, the castle was built with slate quarried on Robben Island and sandstone from Lion's Head, a small mountain, which is sandwiched between Table Mountain and Signal Hill. The original position of the castle was right alongside Table Bay to protect the nascent Dutch settlement from naval invasion. Having long outlived its original function – the seaward wall now stands about 1 km (half a mile) inland after land reclamation – the castle serves as the military headquarters of the Western Cape. Following an extensive program of restoration that took place during 1969–93, it now houses two permanent museums and hosts occasional temporary exhibitions.

Main entrance

🕐 If you visit on a weekday, aim to be at the main gate at 10am or noon for the key ceremony and firing of the signal cannon.

🍴 Situated inside the castle to the left of the main entrance gate, De Goeweneur Restaurant serves inexpensive snacks and light meals that have a Cape Malay influence.

• Map Q5
• Cnr Strand & Darling Rds
• (021) 787 1260
• Open 9am–4pm daily; free guided tours: 11am, noon, 2pm Mon–Sat
• Adm R25, R15 (pensioners), R10 (students and kids)
• De Goeweneur Restaurant: closed Sun • www.castleof goodhope.co.za

Top 10 Features

1. Leeuhek & Moat
2. Main Entrance
3. Block B
4. Governor's & Secunde Houses
5. Kat Balcony
6. William Fehr Collection
7. Military Museum
8. Archway & Old Well
9. Dungeon & Torture Chamber
10. Good Hope Art Workshop

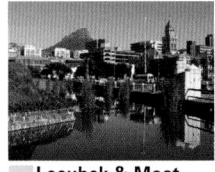

Leeuhek & Moat
The way to the entrance is by crossing a moat *(above)*. On the way is the Leeuhek (Lion's Gate), a sentry portal, which was built in 1720 and crowned with two lion sculptures.

Main Entrance
Built in 1683 to replace the seaward entrance, the main entrance is notable for its bell tower made of imported yellow *ystelsteen* and sculpted masonry depicting a lion with seven arrows to represent the provinces of Netherlands. A key ceremony is held here on weekdays.

The key ceremony

Block B
The castle's oldest section *(below)* to the right of the main entrance dates from the 1660s. A staircase leads to the grassy bastion, offering superb views across the Grand Parade.

4 Governor's & Secunde Houses
Part of the 12-m (39-ft) high inner wall that bisects the courtyard, the Governor's and Secunde houses were built by Simon van der Stel in the 1690s to accommodate himself and his *secunde* (second-in-command).

5 Kat Balcony
This ornate balcony *(left)* has an Anton Anreith bas-relief sculpture. During Dutch colonial times, it was the site for greeting visitors and reading out judicial sentences.

6 William Fehr Collection
Reached via the Kat Balcony, this collection donated by Dr William Fehr includes paintings by Thomas Baines. Other works give an insight into the lives of early settlers.

7 Military Museum
The Cape's military past, from the first clash between Bartolomeu Dias and the locals in 1488 to the 1899–1902 Anglo-Boer War, is documented here *(above)*.

8 Archway & Old Well
The archway connecting the courtyard's two parts is flanked by the covered well that once provided water to the castle's residents, and a memorial to fatalities of World War I.

9 Dungeon & Torture Chamber
This room below the Nassau Bastion was the site where prisoners were tortured, in accordance with the Dutch law that required a confession before sentencing.

City Hall
Cape Town had no city hall prior to 1905, when the foundation was laid in front of the Grand Parade opposite the castle. The Italian Renaissance-style exterior houses interiors with marble staircases and a stained-glass window commemorating King Edward VII. On his release from jail, Mandela made his first public speech from City Hall's balcony.

10 Good Hope Art Workshop
This community project offers a working space to aspiring young artists *(right)*. Visitors are welcome to watch artists at work or view completed canvases.

🔟 Table Mountain

South Africa's most celebrated geographical landmark, Table Mountain dominates the Cape Town skyline from almost every direction. This remarkably flat (hence the name) sandstone plateau basks in golden sunlight or is sometimes swathed in the cloudy shroud locals refer to as the "tablecloth". It is reckoned to be the world's most frequently climbed massif, but most people reach the top using the cableway that first opened in 1929 and has since taken over 18 million passengers to the summit. The main attraction of the summit is the fantastic views, which capture Cape Town and the eponymous Peninsula in their full geological glory. The plateau is also an important sanctuary for fynbos vegetation and associated wildlife, and probably ranks as the "number one" day out from Cape Town.

Table Mountain cable car

❷ The cableway is inoperable on days when mist and cloud settles on the mountain, so if you arrive in Cape Town in good weather, make it your first sightseeing priority.

❶ The Table Mountain Café caters for all tastes, from a breakfast buffet to a gourmet deli, and is set in a great spot for a high-altitude meal at a reasonable price.

• Map H1
• Tafelberg Road
• (021) 424 8181
• Cable cars leave every 10–15 minutes 8:30am–6pm in mid-winter, extending to 10pm midsummer
• Fare R85 one-way or R160 return, kids R45 one-way or R80 return • www.tablemountain.net

Top 10 Features

1. Cableway
2. Upper Cableway Viewpoint
3. Fynbos Vegetation
4. Birdlife
5. Dassies & Other Mammals
6. Dassie, Agama & Klipspringer Trails
7. Sign 15 Viewpoint
8. Abseil Africa
9. Maclear's Beacon
10. Plattklip Gorge Trail

Cableway
The breathtaking 5-minute ride seems too short in this circular cable car, complete with rotating floor and 360-degree views of Cape Town and Table Bay. It travels within nerve-racking inches of the sheer cliff face below the Upper Cableway Station.

Upper Cableway Viewpoint
Emerge from the Upper Cableway Station for a view of the pinnacle of Signal Hill *(left)*, Robben Island in Table Bay and the Hottentots Holland on the eastern horizon.

Fynbos Vegetation
A sweeping glance over Table Mountain's sandstone plateau might be your first exposure to *fynbos*, a heath-like cover whose muted shades are offset by fiery pink proteas, multicoloured disas and spectral silver trees.

Birdlife
The *fynbos* attracts nectar-dependent sunbirds and sugarbirds. The redwing starling *(right)* and chat often visit the summit. Look out for swifts, kestrels and the black eagle.

Dassies & Other Mammals
The Table Mountain Café is a great place to look for the rock hyrax, or dassie, a loveable guinea-pig look-alike often seen basking on the rocky plateau. Other wildlife here include baboon, klipspringer, eland and the gaudy agama lizard.

Dassie, Agama & Klipspringer Trails
These circular, wheel-chair-friendly walks *(left)*, though not teeming with wildlife, offer fantastic views.

Sign 15 Viewpoint
This viewpoint offers sweeping vistas over the mountainous spine of the Cape Peninsula, with glimpses of Simon's Town and Kommetjie through the hills.

Abseil Africa
A must for adventurous travellers is Abseil Africa's 112-m (367-ft) abseil route *(above)* down the ledge of Table Mountain overlooking Camps Bay *(see p49)*.

Tips for Walkers
Table Mountain has several well-marked trails leading to the summit, which have been graded according to their difficulty. All hikers must wear proper walking boots and are advised to check with the Lower Cableway Station before setting out, as weather conditions may deteriorate without warning. Hiking on windy or misty days is not recommended.

Maclear's Beacon
The highest point on Table Mountain *(below)* is an attractive goal for peak-baggers and ramblers alike. There's some great scenery along the way, too.

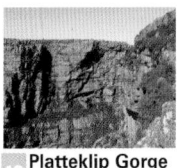

Platteklip Gorge Trail
This non-mechanized alternative to the cableway *(above)* runs to the Lower Cableway Station from Maclear's Beacon.

The walk between the cableway stations via Platteklip Gorge takes 2–4 hours in either direction, depending on your fitness level.

Kirstenbosch National Botanical Garden

Kirstenbosch, one of the world's great botanical gardens, was established in 1913 to protect the immense floral wealth of the Western Cape. On the eastern slopes of Table Mountain, the garden is located on the former private estate of Jan Van Riebeeck (see p35). Later the property of CJ Rhodes, the garden was bequeathed to the nation in 1902. Today, the lower slopes are planted with lush indigenous flora, blending into a natural cover of fynbos *and forest at higher altitudes, accessible by a network of footpaths.*

King Protea flower

Local flora

🌸 Serious botanists should time their visit to coincide with the free guided walks at 10am and 11am from Tuesday to Saturday. Sunset concerts are held on Sundays between December–March.

🍴 The Silvertree Restaurant and Fynbos Deli serves a range of meals and snacks and also picnic lunch baskets to take out onto the lawns.

- Map H2
- Rhodes Drive, Kirstenbosch
- (021) 799 8783
- Open Apr–Aug 8am–6pm daily; Sep–Mar 8am–7pm daily; conservatory 9am–5pm (6pm summer)
- Adm R32, R10 (kids)
- The Silvertree Restaurant and Fynbos Deli: (021) 762 9585
- www.sanbi.org

Top 10 Features

1. Visitors Centre & Shop
2. Conservatory
3. Gondwanaland Garden
4. Mathews Rockery
5. Van Riebeeck's Hedge
6. Cycad Garden & The Dell
7. Fynbos Walk
8. Useful Plants Garden
9. Statue Garden
10. Vlei

1 Visitors Centre & Shop

The centre, which is at the entrance gate, sells a good map of the garden. A souvenir shop *(below)* and the Botanical Society Bookshop, stocked with books about South Africa's flora and fauna, are also located here.

2 Conservatory

The glass-topped conservatory boasts several plants from different South African habitats. At the centre, a spectacular *kokerboom* (tree-sized aloe), typical of the arid Kalahari, rises above other species.

3 Gondwanaland Garden

The rocks on display here *(below)* date back to when there was only one continent, Gondwanaland. The oldest is 3.2 billion years old.

Mathews Rockery

Mathews Rockery has a labyrinthine collection of dry-country plants *(right)* including massive tree aloes. It is at its most spectacular in winter, when the orange aloe blooms attract nectar-eating sunbirds.

5 Van Riebeeck's Hedge

This thick hedge *(left)* of native wild almonds planted by Jan van Riebeeck in 1660 marked the boundary of the fledgling Cape Colony. The cyanide-infused nuts of this plant are inedible.

6 Cycad Garden & The Dell

The garden's oldest part is also the most attractive, with riparian trees, a stream and a pond set below a steep slope of ancient cycads whose spiky leaves evolved over 200 million years ago.

7 Fynbos Walk

This footpath passes through pastel-shaded *fynbos* vegetation unique to the Cape *(centre)*. The salmon-hued proteas found here bloom in winter and spring when they attract the long-tailed Cape sugarbird.

8 Useful Plants Garden

Complete with well-marked signs, this garden has a selection of medicinal plants used to treat everything from headaches and impotence to secondary symptoms of HIV-AIDS.

9 Statue Garden

Situated in the eastern corner of Kirstenbosch, the sprawling Statue Garden is scattered with superb examples of contemporary Zimbabwean and South African stone sculptures *(right)*, created by rising stars of the local art scene.

10 Vlei

A wooden boardwalk crosses the small reed-lined *vlei,* (marsh). It is a magnet for birds, particularly during the summer months when it serves as a breeding ground for the brightly plumed weavers and bishops.

Wildlife in the Gardens

Though best known for its plants, Kirstenbosch also supports varied fauna, with its 200 vertebrate species. The birds range from the Cape sugarbird and orange-breasted sunbird to the spectacular black eagle that breeds on Table Mountain cliffs and gem-like malachite kingfishers that haunt the streams. Mammals include hyraxes and mongooses and two frog species found only on Table Mountain.

🔟 Groot Constantia Wine Estate

Founded by Simon van der Stel in 1685, Groot Constantia is the oldest wine estate in South Africa and possibly the most famous. It boasts a wonderful setting below the Constantiaberg on the Cape Peninsula some 10 km (6 miles) south of central Cape Town. Home to some of the country's most interesting Cape Dutch architecture, it boasts two gabled buildings completed under the late-18th-century proprietorship of Hendrik Cloete. It was under the Cloete family, which owned the farm from 1778 to 1885, that Constantia's dessert wines won international acclaim and the estate became the official supplier to the exiled Napoleon Bonaparte on St Helena. The estate was bought by the Cape Government in 1885 and is now run by a trust.

Orientation Centre

🕐 Most visitors dash in and out to see the museums and sample the wines, but it's worth exploring this lovely estate at leisure on foot.

⭐ For traditional Cape food, the estate has two excellent restaurants.

- Map H2
- Groot Constantia Rd
- Estate: (021) 794 5128; open 10am–5pm, summer 9am–6pm; wine-tasting: adm R25; cellar tours: call ahead for timings; adm R30; www.groot constantia.co.za
- Manor House Museum: (021) 795 5140; open 10am–5pm daily; adm R15; www.iziko.org.za
- The estate's restaurants stay open for dinner

Top 10 Features

1. Wine-Tasting Cellar
2. Historic Gates & Main Drive
3. Manor House Façade
4. Orientation Centre
5. Historic Gardens
6. Manor House Museum
7. Cloete Cellar
8. Historic Bath
9. Jonkershuis
10. Coach House Museum

1 Wine-Tasting Cellar

Just inside the entrance gate, the wine-tasting and sales centre offers excellent wines. The highly praised Grand Constance *(left)* revives the dessert wine tradition that earned the estate its fame.

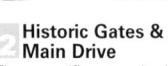

2 Historic Gates & Main Drive

The magnificent main drive leads right up to the main complex, passing through a gate *(below)* that dates from the 18th century.

3 Manor House Façade

Expanding on Van der Stel's house, Hendrik Cloete later added the front gables and commissioned the Anton Anreith sculpture in the niche.

4 Orientation Centre

The orientation centre is a useful first port of call, with its scale model of the estate and informative panels discussing the long history of Constantia.

Historic Gardens
5 Dotted with trees planted in Van der Stel's day, the estate gardens are peaceful and ideal to walk around. They afford views of the vineyards and the sandstone Constantiaberg cliffs.

Manor House Museum
6 This museum in the Manor House is decorated in a style typical of an 18th-century estate owner (left). The furniture and art was donated by collector Alfred de Pass.

Cloete Cellar
7 A narrow structure, the building has South Africa's famous triangular gable and a striking Rococo pediment sculpted by Anton Anreith. Originally a wine cellar, it now displays antique wine storage vessels dating up until the 20th century (right).

Historic Bath
8 This ornate oval pool (below) located on the Constantiaberg slopes is of uncertain origin, but it is similar in style to the gable of the main house which dates from the late 18th century.

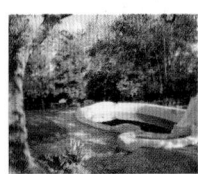

Jonkershuis
9 Expanded from an outbuilding, the thatched Jonkershuis (house of the eldest son or jonkheer) is an attractive Cape Dutch building with a fine restaurant (below).

Coach House Museum
10 In a courtyard behind the Jonkershuis, the Isaacs Transport Collection features old coaches, carts, bicycles and vintage mule and ox wagons (above).

Simon van der Stel
One of the most influential figures of the early colonial era, Simon van der Stel was born in 1639 to Commander Adriaan van der Stel and had a half-Malay mother. He became commander of the Cape in 1679 and was upgraded to Governor in 1691. Van der Stel played a key role in the foundation of Stellenbosch and Simon's Town, both named after him. He retired in 1699 and dedicated himself to the development of Constantia, where he died peacefully in 1712.

TOP 10 Simon's Town and Boulders Beach

South Africa's third-oldest settlement, Simon's Town is named after Governor Simon van der Stel, who selected its harbour as a safe alternative to Table Bay during the stormy Cape winter. The town has a strong historical feel, reflecting its 160-year tenure as Britain's main regional naval base, prior to being handed over to the South African navy in 1957. But far from being the boozy sailors' hangout one might expect, Simon's Town comes across as oddly subdued and genteel. It is lent a distinct character by its wealth of Victorian architecture and lovely location on the steep slopes of the Cape Peninsula above a string of sandy beaches. Most famous of these is Boulders Beach, with its colony of 3,000 penguins.

Boulders Beach signs

🔿 The boardwalk leading straight from the Visitor Centre is good for morning photography. The one leading right is better in the afternoon.

🔾 Dine at the Seaforth Restaurant or Bertha's in the Quayside Mall *(see p81).*

- Map H4
- (021) 786 5880
- Metrorail: (080) 065 6463; www.cape metrorail.co.za
- Simon's Town Museum: Court Rd; (021) 786 3046; open 9am–4pm Mon–Fri, 10am–1pm Sat, 11am–3pm Sun; free
- Naval Museum: Main Rd; (021) 787 4635; 10am–4pm daily • Visitor Centre: (021) 786 2329; call for timings; adm R25 (adults), R5 (kids)
- www.simonstown. com

Top 10 Features

1. Simon's Town Railway
2. Simon's Town Museum
3. South African Naval Museum
4. Historic Mile
5. Jubilee Square and Quay
6. Seaforth Beach
7. Boulders Visitor Centre
8. Foxy Beach
9. Boulders Beach
10. Willis Walk

1 Simon's Town Railway

The Metrorail service *(above)* that begins in Cape Town is one of the world's great suburban train rides, offering a giddying series of beachfront views across False Bay before terminating at Simon's Town's Victorian railway station.

2 Simon's Town Museum

Built as a Governor's Residence, this museum *(right)* houses an exhibition on apartheid's forced removals and a more light-hearted display about a seadog, Just Nuisance.

3 South African Naval Museum

Situated in a dockyard warehouse founded in the 1740s, this specialized museum is known for its life-sized replica of a submarine's interior and ship's bridge, the latter with a simulated rocking motion.

It is advisable to only use the Simon's Town Railway during the day or when travelling as part of a group.

Historic Mile

The concentration of old buildings in Simon's Town is most dense along the so-called Historic Mile – Victorian façades that run along St George's Street (above). Stop by the quaint bar at the Lord Nelson Inn, built in 1802.

Jubilee Square and Quay

At the heart of historic Simon's Town lie palm-lined Jubilee Square and the Quayside Mall which overlook the harbour. Daily boat trips launch from the harbour's jetty to explore False Bay and Seal Island.

Seaforth Beach

Sheltered by rocks and occasionally visited by penguins from neighbouring Boulders, Seaforth (below) offers safe swimming in calm weather. Its popular beachfront restaurant offers a retreat when the wind gets too strong.

Boulders Visitor Centre

Before visiting the penguin colony, stop at the visitor centre at the entrance gate to watch a DVD about these charismatic creatures. There are also displays about marine birds in general.

Foxy Beach

Reached by a pair of boardwalks, sandy Foxy Beach lies at the heart of the African penguin colony (centre). You can glimpse several hundred penguins surfing, squabbling, sunbathing or strutting around.

Boulders Beach

The sheltering rocks after which Boulders is named make it a lovely, secluded spot for a swim. Although it supports fewer penguins than Foxy Beach, you're bound to spot several between the rocks.

Willis Walk

Situated outside the national park, this wheelchair-friendly boardwalk (right) offers opportunities to spot penguins and their offspring, and fynbos birds such as Cape canaries and martins.

Boulders Beach Orientation

Boulders lies to the south of Simon's Town and is accessed from the main road to Cape Point via Seaforth or Bellevue Road. Foxy and Boulders Beaches lie within an annexe of Table Mountain National Park and are entered via two separate gates. The Boulders Visitor Centre is at the Foxy Beach gate. Willis Walk, which connects the two gates, is outside the park and is open at all times.

🔟 Cape of Good Hope Nature Reserve

Though Cape Point is not the southern-most point in Africa, most visitors walk away with the distinct sensation that they've seen the end of the continent, such is the scenic drama of the storm-battered headland, whose precipitous cliffs rise to 250 m (820 ft) from the vast blue sea. The Cape of Good Hope (now part of Table Mountain National Park) is also of interest for its wealth of fauna, which ranges from the endemic bontebok and Cape mountain zebra to breeding cormorants and passing whales. The Cape's nature reserve has a cover of pastel-hued fynbos (see box on p78), which comprises more plant species than are indigenous to the entire British Isles.

Cape of Good Hope

🐾 Semi-habituated baboons lurk around the car park below Cape Point. Though they are a fascinating sight, baboons can be dangerous if you are carrying food.

🍽 The Two Oceans Restaurant adjacent to the car park serves mid-range meals during the day. Tasty ostrich platters are served at the Cape Point Ostrich Farm.

• Map H5
• Table Mountain National Park
• (021) 780 9207
• Open Oct–Mar 6am–6pm, Apr–Sep 7am–5pm • Adm R60
• www.capepoint.co.za
• Cape Point Ostrich Farm: (021) 780 9294; half-hourly tours 10am–5pm; tour R30, www.cape pointostrichfarm.com
• Funicular: R40 return

Top 10 Features

1. Buffelsfontein Visitor Centre
2. Kanonkop Walk
3. Rooikrans
4. Cape Point Lighthouse
5. Gifkommetjie Circular Drive
6. Platboom Beach
7. Climb/Funicular to Cape Point
8. Bordjiesdrif
9. Cape of Good Hope Footpath
10. Cape Point Ostrich Farm

Buffelsfontein Visitor Centre

This Cape Dutch farmhouse *(above)* should be your first stop if you plan to explore the area. Apart from a stock of books and leaflets about the reserve, it also contains a natural history museum.

Kanonkop Walk

A short walking trail that starts at Buffelsfontein, Kanonkop Walk leads to the old signal cannon after which it is named. It passes a 19th-century lime kiln and offers some splendid views across False Bay *(right)*. Look out for the blue disa that flowers here in January and February.

A view of Cape Point

Rooikrans

Just 1 km (half a mile) from the main road to Cape Point, this superb viewpoint is the best spot for seasonal whale watching. A footpath leads to the rocky beach below.

Cape Point Lighthouse

Built in 1913–19 with rocks carried by hand from the present-day car park, this is South Africa's brightest lighthouse *(above)*. But the draw here is the stunning scenery, and this seldom disappoints – rain or shine.

Gifkommetjie Circular Drive

This road loop leads through subtly shaded fields of *fynbos* to a ridge studded with mushroom-like balancing rock formations. The views are stunning and energetic visitors can follow the little-used 3-hour walking trail to Hoek van Bobejaan (Baboon's Corner).

Platboom Beach

This little-visited beach is ideal for swimming. It is reached by a road that passes a giant cross erected in 1965 to commemorate Bartolomeu Dias' landing in 1488 *(see p34)*.

Climb/Funicular to Cape Point

The final ascent to spectacular Cape Point involves hiking a steep footpath, or taking the funicular *(above)* – a rope-supported railway designed for such gradients.

Bordjiesdrif

The tidal pools at this rocky beach are good for marine life and the artificial rock pool above the beach is safe to swim in. Sights include a cross erected to honour Vasco da Gama's landing in 1497, and the Black Rock, an igneous formation.

Cape Point Ostrich Farm

Immediately outside the park entrance, this child-friendly private ostrich farm offers an opportunity to get up close with the world's largest birds *(below)*. It is a good place to pick up ostrich-derived souvenirs, from giant hollowed eggs to plush leatherware.

Cape of Good Hope Footpath

If the windswept ascent to Cape Point hasn't robbed you of breath, try the 90-minute return trail *(above)* from the car park to the Cape of Good Hope beach below, offering stirring views of the lighthouse and good marine birdwatching.

Whales in False Bay

Between July and November, the whales that pass through False Bay can be observed from Rooikrans and other beaches along the reserve's eastern seaboard. The most common is the southern right whale, which typically reaches a length of around 15 m (49 ft). It is also possible to glimpse Bryde's whales, humpback whales and killer whales (orcas). Call (021) 787 9140 for news of recent sightings.

^{TOP}10 Stellenbosch

Founded by Simon van der Stel in 1679, Stellenbosch is the second oldest town in South Africa, and arguably the most beautiful. Running north from the banks of the Eerste River below the Jonkershoek Mountains, the stately avenues of this university town are lined with venerable Cape Dutch buildings and the shady trees that earned it the nickname of Eikestad (Town of Oaks). This old-world ambience is offset by a contemporary array of restaurants, cafés, bars and shops. It is worth spending a night here to explore the surrounding Winelands; the short drive to nearby Franschhoek via the Helshoogte Pass is packed with must-see sights (see pp30–31).

Display at Rupert Museum

Lanzerac Estate

🍴 Restaurants see p90.

- • Map D2
- • Toy & Miniature Museum: (021) 887 2948; adm R5
- • Rupert Museum: Lower Dorp St; (021) 888 3344; adm R20
- • Village Museum: 18 Ryneveld St; (021) 887 2948; open daily; adm R20 (adults) R5 (kids); www.stelmus. co.za • Botanical Garden: Cnr Neethling & Van Riebeeck Rd; open 8am–5pm; free
- • Bergkelder Wine Cellar: Adam Tas Rd; (021) 809 8025; tasting 8am–5pm Mon–Fri, 9am–2pm Sat; R15; tour (tasting incl.) R25; www. bergkelder.co.za
- • Lanzerac Estate: Jonkershoek Rd; (021) 887 1132; tasting 8:30am–5pm Mon–Fri, 10am–2pm Sat, 11am–3pm Sun; R15; www.lanzerac wines.co.za

Top 10 Features

1. The Braak
2. Toy & Miniature Museum
3. Dorp Street
4. Oom Samie se Winkel
5. Rupert Museum
6. Stellenbosch Village Museum
7. Moederkerk
8. Botanical Garden
9. Bergkelder Wine Cellar
10. Lanzerac Estate

The Braak
The village green (*braak*) is enclosed by historic buildings, notably the Anglican Church of St Mary (1852) *(above)*, with its combined Neo-Gothic and Cape Dutch influences, and the Rhenish Church, (1823) with a Baroque pulpit.

Toy & Miniature Museum
Housed in a Rhenish parsonage, this museum has tiny houses (right), antique dolls and a re-created Blue Train travelling from a miniature Stellenbosch to Matjiesfontein.

Dorp Street
The best preserved road in town, Dorp Street is lined with pre-20th-century Cape Dutch buildings. The finest façades can be seen between the junctions of Herte and Drostdy Streets.

The museums stay open 9:30am–5pm Mon–Fri and mornings only on Sat; call ahead if you plan to visit on weekends.

Oom Samie se Winkel

Named after former owner Oom (Uncle) Samie Volsteedt, this landmark store *(see p86)* stocks home-made confectionary and Africana *(below)*.

Rupert Museum

To the town's southwest, this museum of South African art exhibits works by artists such as Irma Stern and Moses Kotler.

Stellenbosch Village Museum

Each of this museum's period-furnished houses *(below)* represent phases in the town's development; the most recent dating from the 1830s.

Moederkerk

Opposite the Village Museum, on the site of the original Dutch Reformed Church that burned down in 1710, stands the imposing Moederkerk (Mother Church), a tall Neo-Gothic construction whose steeple was completed in 1866.

Botanical Garden

The small but leafy Botanical Garden, the town's best-kept secret, particularly notable for its collections of *fynbos* plants and dry-country succulents from Namibia.

Bergkelder Wine Cellar

This distinctive building nestled below the Papegaaiberg has more than 200 wines. Taste the Cape's finest produce in the atmospheric cellar.

Lanzerac Estate

This is the closest estate to Stellenbosch. First planted with vines in 1692, it was then known as Scoongezicht (Clean Face). Excellent wines and a restaurant *(right)* make it worth a detour.

University of Stellenbosch

South Africa's premier Afrikaans university started life in 1866 as the Stellenbosch Gymnasium in a building that still stands on Dorp Street. The university alumni include four of South Africa's presidents (Jan Smuts, DF Malan, JB Hertzog and HF Verwoed) and anti-apartheid activists such as Beyers Naudé and Heinrich Grosskopf. The town's Botanical Garden was founded by the university in 1922.

Left **Tasting room at Tokara** Centre **Wine from Tokara** Right **View from Hillcrest Berry Orchard**

🔟 Stellenbosch To Franschhoek

1 Tokara and Delaire Wine Estates

These estates, perched on the rim of Helshoogte Pass, are best saved for the end of the day, when superb views over the Winelands can be enjoyed at sunset over a glass of local bubbly. ◈ *Tokara: Map E2; Helshoogte Rd; (021) 808 5900; tasting: 9am–5pm Mon–Fri, 10am–3pm Sat, Sun; tasting free; www.tokara.co.za • Delaire: Map E2; Helshoogte Pass Rd; (021) 885 8160; tasting: 10am–6pm Mon–Sun; tasting adm; www.delairewinery.co.za*

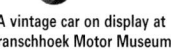

A vintage car on display at Franschhoek Motor Museum

2 Hillcrest Berry Orchards

About 10 km (6 miles) from Stellenbosch, Hillcrest cultivates seven types of berries. Its confections can be tasted at the coffee shop or bought at the gift shop. ◈ *Map E2 • (021) 885 1629 • Helshoogte Pass Rd • Open 9am–5pm daily • www.hillcrestberries.co.za*

3 Pniel

Founded by the Berlin Mission Society in 1834 to house former slaves, picturesque Pniel, below the Simonsberg, remained zoned for Coloureds under apartheid despite its prime location. Landmarks include a 19th-century church and the 1992 Freedom Monument commemorating the emancipation of slaves. ◈ *Map E2*

4 Boschendal Wine Estate

Located at the gateway to the Franschhoek Valley, this iconic estate's renowned picnic baskets and wines make for a decadent lunch. ◈ *Map E2 • (021) 870 4210/1 • Open Oct–Mar 8:30am–6:30pm daily; Apr–Sep 9am–4:30pm daily; cellar tours: 10:30am & 11:30am • www.boschendal.co.za*

5 Franschhoek Motor Museum

Situated on the prestigious L'Ormarins Estate, this museum is a magnet for car enthusiasts. The collection includes an 1898 Beeston motor tricycle and a 2005 Ferrari Enzo. ◈ *Map F2 • R45 towards Franschhoek • (021) 874 9000 • Open 10am–4pm Tue–Fri, 10am–3pm Sat–Sun • Adm • www.fmm.co.za*

Vineyards at Boschendal Wine Estate

The picnic area at the Boschendal Wine Estate is closed on Sun from May–Oct.

Franschhoek Winery

Situated to the right as you enter Franschhoek, this private winery has a large cellar. Ideal for serious wine buyers who prefer tasting a wide selection in one sitting, the winery often has some good special deals going too. ◈ Map F2 • Main Rd • (021) 876 2086 • Open 9:30am–5pm Mon–Fri, 10am–4pm Sat, 11am–3pm Sun • Tasting adm

Mont Rochelle

A 5-minute drive – or a steep half-hour walk – from Franschhoek, this small wine estate boasts impressively thatched Cape Dutch buildings. The estate offers a perfect view over the Franschhoek Valley and Middagkrans Mountains, which is best enjoyed from one of the two fine restaurants located on the property. ◈ Map F2 • Dassenberg Rd • (021) 876 2770 • www.montrochelle.co.za

Huguenot Monument

A stone monument built on the outskirts of Franschhoek in 1938–48, this monument commemorates the arrival of the Huguenots in 1688. The three high arches represent the holy trinity, while a statue of a woman on a globe displays various religious symbols. ◈ Map F3 • Lambrecht Rd • Open 9am–5pm daily • Adm

Huguenot Memorial Museum

This excellent museum documents the daily life of the French settlers who gave Franschhoek its name and advanced the production of wine in the Cape. ◈ Map F3 • Lambrecht Rd • (021) 876 2532 • Open 9am–5pm Mon–Sat, 2pm–5pm Sun • Adm • www. museum.co.za

Dutch Reformed Church

Franschhoek's architectural gem, the Dutch Reformed Church was built in 1848. Set below the surrounding mountains, the church's whitewashed gables and 19th-century bell tower make a pretty, pastoral picture. ◈ Map F2 • Huguenot Rd

Dutch Reformed Church

The Huguenots

The Huguenots were French Protestants who fled France to escape Catholic persecution during Louis XIV's reign. Franschhoek, then known as Olifantshoek (Elephant's Corner), is a legacy to their influx to the Cape in 1688. Due partly to a Dutch East India Company (VOC) edict that Dutch should be the exclusive language of education, local government and commerce, the Huguenots swiftly integrated into the established settler culture. By 1750, French was barely spoken in the Cape, but the Huguenot influence was a major contributor to South Africa's emergence as a top wine producer. Furthermore, many Afrikaans surnames are of French origin. While some like De Villiers and Malan have survived unchanged, others have been bastardized, such as Cronjé (Cronier) and Nel (Neél).

Left **Foundation of the UDF** Right **The Anglo-Boer War**

🔟 Moments in History

1 Prehistory
The earliest signs of human habitation along Table Bay, dating back 1.4 million years, consist of Stone Age tools of the Acheulean culture. San hunter-gatherers arrived around 30,000 years ago and left a legacy of rock art sites, notably the Cederberg Mountains north of Cape Town. Khoikhoi pastoralists first arrived with their fat-tailed sheep around 2,000 years ago.

2 The Portuguese Arrive
In 1488, Portuguese navigator Bartolomeu Dias became the first European to round the Cape. This led to a succession of clashes with the Khoikhoi that culminated in Captain d'Almeida's death in Table Bay in 1510.

3 Foundation of Cape Town
In 1652, Jan van Riebeeck, an employee of the Dutch East India Company (VOC), founded a victual station in Table Bay to provide fresh produce to passing VOC ships. Within a century, Cape Town was home to settlers from Europe, though slaves outnumbered free citizens.

4 British Occupation and the Great Trek
The relatively liberal governance of Cape Town by the British in 1795 led to the emancipation of slaves in 1834. This so angered slave-owning Boers (Dutch farmers) that over 12,000 moved north in the Great Trek of 1836–43, where they founded Boer Republics, notably the Free State and Transvaal.

5 Anglo-Boer War and Unionization
The Anglo-Boer War of 1899–1902 was initiated by English imperialists to gain control of the Johannesburg goldfields. This bloody three-year engagement led to the formation of the Union of South Africa in 1910 which comprised the Cape, Natal, Transvaal and the Free State. Former Boer general Louis Botha became the first prime minister.

6 Foundation of Apartheid
After the National Party (NP) was voted in by the electorate in 1948, parliamentary acts formalized racial inequities into the ideological monolith apartheid ("separateness").

Nelson Mandela, former ANC leader

 Preceding pages **View of flat-topped Table Mountain**

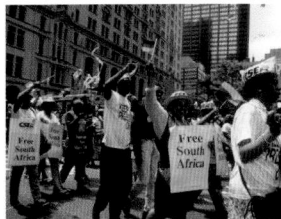

Union workers protesting against apartheid

Sharpeville Massacre and Rivonia Trial

Resistance to apartheid was galvanized by the police massacre of 69 civilians at a peaceful protest at Sharpeville in 1960. This led to the formation of Umkhonto we Sizwe (the armed wing of the banned ANC) under Nelson Mandela, who was convicted of treason along with other anti-apartheid leaders in the Rivonia Trial of 1962–3.

Foundation of the UDF

In 1983, some 15,000 anti-apartheid activists congregated at Mitchell's Plain to form the United Democratic Front (UDF), effectively the domestic representative of the ANC in apartheid's dying years.

Release of Nelson Mandela

President FW de Klerk lifted the ban on the ANC in February 1990, and Mandela was released from prison after 27 years. He made his first speech outside Cape Town's City Hall (see p17).

Democracy

In May 1994, the ANC swept to victory in South Africa's first fully democratic elections, after securing eight of the nine provinces, the exception being the Western Cape, the last stronghold of the NP. Mandela was inaugurated as president.

Top 10 Famous South Africans

1 Jan van Riebeeck
Founder of Cape Town, Van Riebeeck was commander of the Cape until 1662.

2 Simon van der Stel
Governor of the Cape 1679–99, Van der Stel was the founder of Stellenbosch and prime mover behind the development of the Constantia wineries.

3 Cecil John Rhodes
British mining magnate Rhodes founded the diamond company De Beers, and was prime minister of the Cape from 1890 to 1895.

4 Breyten Breytenbach (b. 1939)
This Cape Town-educated poet and novelist, imprisoned for anti-apartheid activities, now resides in France.

5 Nelson Mandela
South Africa's most famous son was incarcerated in prisons around Cape Town for 27 years *(see p13)*.

6 Archbishop Desmond Tutu
This Nobel Peace Prize winner served as Anglican Archbishop of Cape Town between 1985 and 1995 *(see p9)*.

7 Brenda Fassie
The "Madonna of the Townships" was a popular recording artist prior to her drug-related death in 2004.

8 Jacques Kallis
One of South Africa's greatest cricketers.

9 Benni McCarthy
This footballer has scored 29 international goals.

10 JM Coetzee
Recipient of the 2003 Nobel Prize for Literature and two-time Booker Prize winner.

Left **View of Table Mountain from Bloubergstrand** Right **Vistas along Chapman's Peak Drive**

🔟 Viewpoints

1 Table Mountain Upper Cableway

Within 15 minutes of the Upper Cableway station, a succession of viewpoints reveal the geography of the Western Cape, from nearby Signal Hill and City Bowl to surf-splashed Robben Island and False Bay, all overshadowed by the Hottentots Holland Mountains. No less impressive are the views across the Cape Peninsula's mountainous spine to Cape Point.

2 Signal Hill

Rising between the City Bowl and Sea Point, flat-topped 350-m (1,148-ft) Signal Hill is an extension of a taller, hornlike rock formation known as Lion's Head. Accessible by car or foot, the picnic site affords a stunning view over the city centre, especially at sunset with the red western Atlantic sky. Many visitors like to visit in time for the firing of the Noon Gun, a tradition that dates back to the 18th century *(see p62)*.

3 Rhodes Memorial

Situated on the eastern slopes of Table Mountain, this is a rather bombastic memorial. The views over the Cape Flats to distant Helderberg and the Hottentots Holland Mountains are best enjoyed from the adjacent coffee shop *(see p73)*.

4 Chapman's Peak Drive

One of the world's most spectacular marine drives, this toll road was constructed in 1915–22 along the band of shale that divides the granite base of Chapman's Peak from the overlying sandstone. It winds along the mountainside between Hout Bay and Noordhoek with viewpoints along the way. Stop to admire the sheer cliffs of Chapman's Peak and the Atlantic battering the shore below *(see p78)*. ⊗ Map G3 • Light vehicles: adm • www.chapmanspeakdrive.co.za

5 Cape Point

Situated at the southern tip of the Cape Peninsula within the Cape of Good Hope Nature Reserve *(see pp26–7)*, Cape Point is reached via a steep footpath or a chuffing funicular. The views include windswept cliffs and Atlantic-battered beaches to an open seascape that stretches all the way south to Antarctica *(see pp26–7)*.

Views of Cape Town from Signal Hill

Rooikrans

6 Part of the Cape of Good Hope Nature Reserve, this under-utilized viewpoint provides a thrilling north-facing vantage on the False Bay seaboard. There are great whale watching opportunities between June and November *(see p26)*.

Bloubergstrand

7 About 10 km (6 miles) north of Cape Town, the Bloubergstrand beach hems in Table Bay on the West Coast. This "Blue Mountain Beach" is named after the flat-topped Table Mountain, which looms over its sandy expanse. Usually at its prettiest in the morning, the beach is worth visiting in the afternoon as well, when you can enjoy the vista from alfresco cafés *(see p61)*.

Tokara Wine Estate

8 At the crest of Helshoogte Pass, this wine and olive estate boasts perhaps the most scenic location in the Winelands. The views stretch across eucalyptus-swathed slopes to False Bay and – on a clear day – distant Table Mountain. Best enjoyed with a chilled glass of the estate's crisp Zondernaam Sauvignon Blanc *(see p30)*.

Franschhoek Pass

9 This pass is often ignored by tourists because it leads to remote Villiersdorp rather than trendy

The vineyards surrounding the Tokara Estate

Stellenbosch. But it is worth following this road for a couple of kilometres to take in the lovely views over the thatched rooftops and the expansive vineyards that are located in the Franschhoek Valley *(see p31)*.

Paarl Mountain

10 The world's second-largest granite outcrop, Paarl Mountain is on the outskirts of Paarl. The mountain is at its most spectacular at dusk when it glows like a pearl, from where it gets its name. A 2-hour trail leads to the top of the outcrop. Views from this point stretch to the *fynbos*-covered lower slopes and the bustling town, and extend to the surrounding vineyards and the Drakenstein (Dragon's Stone) Mountain's outline. ◈ *Map E1*

Left **Scratch Patch** Centre **A cheetah, Spier Wine Farm** Right **Monkey Jungle at World of Birds**

🔟 Activities for Children

1 Monkey Town Primate Sanctuary

Most of the primates of this sanctuary have been rescued from captivity. The species ranging from chimps to the pygmy marmoset, are housed in a large, green enclosure surrounded by a viewing walkway. ❦ *Map D4*
• *Mondeor Rd, Somerset West*
• *(021) 858 1060 • Open 9am–5pm daily • www.monkeys.co.za*

2 Scratch Patch

With branches in Simon's Town and the V&A Waterfront, Scratch Patch resembles a psychedelic gravel heap. A profusion of colourful, tumble-polished gemstones – including **Macaw parrots** tiger's eye, lapis lazuli, blue lace agate, rose quartz, amethyst and jasper – is scattered on the floor. For a small fee, kids (and adults) can "scratch" around and fill bagfuls to take home. ❦ *The V&A Waterfront: Map A2; Dock Rd; (021) 419 9429; open 9am–5:30pm daily • Simon's Town: Map H4; Dido Rd; (021) 786 2020; open 8:30am–4:45pm Mon–Fri, 9am–5:30pm Sat–Sun • www.scratchpatch.co.za*

3 Iziko Planetarium

The domed planetarium, part of the National Museum complex in the Company's Garden, features daily shows introducing the brilliant southern night sky. Other specialized shows include programmes for kids *(see p9)*.

4 World of Birds

Situated in Hout Bay, World of Birds is Africa's largest bird park with over 400 indigenous and exotic species, including parrots and barbets, in walk-through aviaries. Visitors can glimpse the various aspects of birdlife, right from eggs in incubation to the feeding of chicks. The park also features reptiles and mammals, especially monkeys, in its Monkey Jungle *(see p79)*.

5 Tygerberg Zoo

The only zoo in the Cape Town area, Tygerberg is situated in the Winelands and houses 1,400 individual animals from 280 species. The focus is on primates,

A lion at Tygerberg Zoo

small antelope and tortoises. Big cats are also well represented. The zoo doubles as a breeding centre for endangered wildlife, and also has a farmyard for children. ✪ *Map D2* • *15 km (9 miles) from Stellenbosch, btwn Cape Town and Paarl* • *(021) 884 4494* • *Open 9am–5pm daily* • *Adm*

Penguins at the Two Oceans Aquarium

Spier Wine Farm
The most child friendly of the Cape wine estates, Spier has a playground near the Deli and an enclosed one across the river. Other attractions include tame cheetahs, a centre for birds of prey, and pony rides *(see p83)*.

Ratanga Junction
This vast theme park to the north of the city has rides for the entire family, including an 18-m (59-ft) water ride (Monkey Falls) and the Cobra roller coaster. Options such as dodgem cars, train rides and a mini-Ferris are more child-oriented. There is also a nine-hole putt-putt course and a stone patch (similar to Scratch Patch). ✪ *Map B2* • *N1 Sable Rd turn-off* • *(021) 550 8500* • *Open 10am–5pm daily (only for the Western Cape school holidays)* • *Adm for rides*
• *www.ratanga.co.za*

Drakenstein Lion Park
The best place to see lions in the Cape Town area is this park near Paarl, which provides sanctuary to captive-born lions that cannot be introduced into the wild. Viewing platforms overlook large enclosures that house the 15 lions. Include a trip to nearby Butterfly World when you visit *(see p84)*.

Two Oceans Aquarium
South Africa's leading aquarium boasts an extraordinary diversity of marine life both from the chilly Atlantic and the warmer Indian Ocean on the east coast. The penguins, sharks and giant rays are a favourite with children. A free activity centre hosts puppet shows and a variety of arts and crafts. Visit at feeding time *(see p10)*.

Imhoff Farm
This restored 18th-century farm on the Atlantic seaboard en route to Cape Point has domestic animals roaming the farmyard. Activities for kids include pony and camel rides. A pleasant coffee shop sells home-made cheese. ✪ *Map G4* • *Kommetjie* • *(021) 783 4545* • *Open 10am–5pm Tue–Sun* • *www.imhofffarm.co.za*

Feeding time for lions in the Drakenstein Lion Park is at 4pm on Mon, Wed and Fri.

Left **Kirstenbosch National Botanical Garden** Right **Mountain biking, De Hoop Nature Reserve**

Parks and Reserves

Table Mountain National Park

Proclaimed as a national park in 1998, this park amalgamates a series of reserves that follow the Cape Peninsula south to Cape Point. This rich biodiversity, with an estimated 2,000 plant species and fauna from the Himalayan tahr to endemic birds and frogs, thrives within metropolitan Cape Town. ◈ *Map T4 • (021) 701 8692 • Opening hrs vary for each reserve • Adm for select reserves • www.sanparks.org*

Kirstenbosch National Botanical Garden

On the eastern slopes of Table Mountain, these landscaped gardens showcase South Africa's peerless floral varieties, and can be explored on a network of well-maintained, wheelchair-friendly footpaths *(see pp20–21).*

Silvermine Nature Reserve

The least publicized of the three main blocs that comprise Table Mountain National Park, Silvermine is a refreshing alternative to the Table Mountain Cableway. The Silvermine River Walk provides an introduction to *fynbos* vegetation and birdlife, while the steeper walk to Noordhoek Peak and Elephant's Eye Cave offers oceanic views. ◈ *Map B4 • (021) 701 8692 • Open May–Aug 8am–5pm; Sep–Apr 7am–6pm • www.tmnp.co.za*

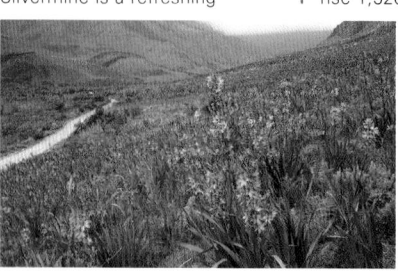

Cape Cormorant

De Hoop Nature Reserve

This reserve supports plant, bird and mammal species in the world's largest surviving tract of coastal *fynbos*. It stretches inland to the craggy Potsberg, a breeding site for the endangered Cape vulture. Used mostly by hikers and cyclists, it can also be explored by road *(see p95).*

Jonkershoek and Assegaaibosch Nature Reserves

A ramblers' paradise, these adjoining reserves protect the Jonkershoek Mountains, which rise 1,526 m (5,005 ft) on the eastern outskirts of Stellenbosch. Apart from the wildlife and montane *fynbos*, it also offers day walks, ranging from a stroll through the Assegaaibosch wildflower garden, to the challenging 18-km (9-mile) Swartboskloof Trail *(see p83).*

Watsonia flowers in spring at Jonkershoek Nature Reserve

6 Rietvlei Nature Reserve

Located in suburban Milnerton and Table View, Rietvlei is one of the top bird-watching sites in Cape Town and provides protection to the Diep River floodplain, which attracts freshwater and marine birds.

Harold Porter National Botanical Garden

Almost 200 species have been recorded to date. Between October and March, there is an influx of migrant waders. There is a hide and footpath here. ◉ *Map T4 • Grey Ave, Table View • (021) 557 5509 • Open 7:30am–5pm daily • Adm • www.friendsofrietvlei.co.za*

7 Harold Porter National Botanical Garden

This botanical garden in Betty's Bay is an excellent place to get familiar with *fynbos* flora, including the *Disa uniflora* in its natural habitat, proteas, ericas and orchids. The birdlife found in the garden is an added attraction for avid birdwatchers, with most *fynbos* endemics well-represented *(see p98)*.

8 Paarl Mountain Nature Reserve

Situated on the outskirts of Paarl, with a mix of montane *fynbos* and indigenous forests, this reserve protects the granite domes, which give the town its name. Good for a bracing walk, the spot is frequented by anglers and mountain bikers. ◉ *Map E1 • Jan Phillips Mountain Dr, Paarl • (021) 872 3658 • Open 7am–7pm daily • Fee for use of a vehicle*

9 West Coast National Park

Centred on the sheltered Langebaan Lagoon, this sprawling marine park is popular with bird and watersport enthusiasts. Apart from the coastal scenery, attractions include dry-country wildlife such as oryx and springbok. Visit in August–September, when the blooming wildflowers in the Postberg section are a stunning sight *(see p96)*.

10 Bird Island

This rocky outcrop, lying offshore of the west coast port of Lambert's Bay, is the world's only accessible breeding colony of the striking Cape gannet birds. The island also hosts Cape cormorants, penguins and seals. ◉ *Map S1 • Lambert's Bay • (0861) 227 362 8873 • Open 7am–5pm daily, summer 7am–7pm daily • Adm • www. capenature.co.za*

Left **Seals sunning themselves at Seal Island, Hout Bay** Right **Harbour cruise**

🔟 Wildlife Experiences

1 Birdwatching at Rondevlei Bird Sanctuary

This large wetland on the Cape Flats is easily the best place to spot waterbirds in suburban Cape Town. Among the 230 species recorded are the great white pelican, African spoonbill and various herons. Two perpetually grunting hippos were introduced in 1982. ◈ *Map I3*
• *Perth Rd, Rondevlei* • *(021) 706 2404*
• *Open 7:30am–5pm, closes 7pm Dec & Jan* • *Adm* • *www.rondevlei.co.za*

2 Harbour Cruise

Operators on the V&A Waterfront offer cruises through Table Bay, with a near certainty of sighting Cape fur seals and various gulls and terns. On a good day you might also catch sight of dolphins *(see pp10–11)*.

3 Dassies on Table Mountain

Watch the endearing semi-tame dassies (hyraxes) sunbathing on Table Mountain. Resembling guinea pigs, but larger and sharper-toothed, these oddball creatures are dwarfish relics of a group of ungulates that dominated the African herbivore niche about 35 million years ago *(see pp18–19)*.

4 Penguin Colony, Boulders Beach

Waddling around like tipsy tuxedoed waiters, these flightless birds are a firm fixture on the tourist itinerary. Amazingly, the 3,000-strong Boulder colony was founded by two breeding pairs in 1982 *(see pp24–5)*.

5 Seal Island, Near Hout Bay

A flat granite outcrop 6 km (4 miles) offshore, this island supports the Western Cape's largest seal colony (up to 75,000 individuals), along with some penguins and three species of cormorant. Though visitors are not allowed to mingle with the animals, boat tours run past the seal-lined shores *(see p79)*.

6 Cape of Good Hope

The most southerly sector of Table Mountain National Park, the Cape of Good Hope boasts spectacular oceanic viewpoints. It also offers excellent wildlife watching – localized endemics such as bontebok, grysbok and mountain zebra coexist with the chacma baboon, eland and small grey mongoose *(see pp26–7)*.

African penguin on Boulders Beach

Caged shark dives

Land-Based Whale Watching

The Western Cape has the world's best land-based whale watching. Cliffs at Hermanus, De Hoop and False Bay offer vantage points to view the southern right whale breaching in the deep, sheltered bays. ◈ *Peak season Jun–Nov; calving season Jul–Aug*

Caged Shark Dives

Caged dives to see the great white shark in rapacious action rank as the ultimate submarine wildlife encounter for thrill-seekers. However, this baiting of sharks has been condemned by conservationists; it may also be the cause of the increased attacks on swimmers and surfers. ◈ *Shark Cage Diving: (021) 461 6583 • www.sharkcagediving.co.za*

Scuba Diving and Snorkelling

The kelp forests and deep tidal pools of the Atlantic offer some excellent opportunities for diving into the deep to glimpse weird and wonderful marine creatures.

Inverdoorn Game Reserve

A spectacular reserve in the immensity of the Karoo and only a few hours' drive from Cape Town. It is rich in wildlife, including lions, cheetahs, giraffe, antelope and white rhino. A range of leisure activities are also available. ◈ *Map U4 • off R46 • (214) 244 639 • www.inverdoorn.com*

Top 10 Endemic Flora and Fauna

1 King Protea
This pineapple-sized salmon-pink bloom is South Africa's national flower.

2 Red Disa
The "Pride of Table Mountain", this pretty red flower blooms Dec–Jan.

3 Silver Tree
Restricted to the Cape Peninsula, this odd protea-affiliated tree has silver-haired stems and cone-like flowers.

4 African Penguin
The only penguin that breeds in South Africa. Two other sub-Antarctic species turn up occasionally on the Cape's beaches.

5 Bontebok
This beautifully marked antelope was on the verge of extinction in the 20th century.

6 Cape Dwarf Chameleon
The most readily observed of four chameleon species from the Western Cape mountains.

7 Cape Mountain Zebra
Rescued from extinction, the Cape Mountain Zebra has fared better than its close relative, the quagga, hunted out in the 19th century.

8 Cape Sugarbird
This long-tailed *fynbos* dweller belongs to a family whose range is limited to South Africa and Zimbabwe.

9 Orange-Breasted Sunbird
Dazzling nectar-eater limited to flowering *fynbos* habitats.

10 Table Mountain Ghost Frog
Seldom seen, this club-fingered frog is known from just the seven specific streams on Table Mountain.

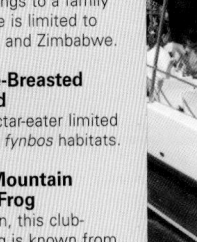

Fynbos *is a type of heath-like scrub cover confined to the Cape coast of South Africa.*

Left **Beach huts at Muizenberg** Right **The shores of Boulders Beach**

🔟 Beaches

1 Clifton Beach
Situated within easy walking distance of Sea Point and Green Point, perennially fashionable Clifton is the closest swimming beach to the city centre. Of the four sandy coves divided by granite outcrops, Fourth Beach has the best facilities, including changing rooms, public toilets, snack and soda kiosks. Deck chairs and umbrellas are available for daily rental. The waters are relatively chilly and the undertow should not be underestimated *(see p62)*.

2 Camps Bay
Overlooked by the spectacular Twelve Apostles formation on the western face of Table Mountain, this wide, sandy beach lies alongside the main road through Camps Bay below a row of trendy street cafés, restaurants and bars. A popular haunt with families over the holidays, it is generally quieter at other times. Deck chairs and umbrellas are available for hire at this beach *(see p61)*.

3 Sandy Bay
Protected by high dunes and dotted with secluded rocky coves for sunbathing, Sandy Bay near Llandudno has long been a semi-official nudist beach. It also hosts something of a gay scene, though by no means exclusively so. It is relatively inaccessible by public transport, and often too chilly for swimming. 🌐 *Map G2*

4 Noordhoek
Set below spectacular Chapman's Peak *(see p61)*, Noordhoek is a seemingly endless arc of glorious white sand near Kommetjie. Though too exposed to the elements to host much of a beach scene, it attracts walkers, birdwatchers and horse riders. Perfect for a long seaside stroll *(see p78)*.

5 Muizenberg
Along the northern shore of False Bay, Muizenberg was Cape Town's trendiest beach in the 1960s, but its glitz has now faded. Still, it is usually safe for swimming and excellent for surfing. The varied facilities, including a protected pool, water-slides, miniature golf course, snack shops and colourful changing rooms, ensure that the beach remains a favourite with families. It is very accessible by train from the city centre *(see p77)*.

Camps Bay with Lion's Head in the background

The rocky shores of Seaforth Beach

Cape of Good Hope
6 Set below Cape Point, this windswept beach is arguably the most beautiful on the peninsula. As well as attracting sunbathers and swimmers, the Cape is also a magnet for walkers and nature enthusiasts (see pp26–7).

Boulders Beach
7 This is a lovely, secluded beach on the southern fringe of the penguin colony (see p42). Enjoy the company of these remarkable birds, who bustle fearlessly around the same rocks where tourists sunbathe. An entrance fee is required (see p25).

Seaforth Beach
8 Like nearby Boulders, this beach, within walking distance of Simon's Town, is hemmed in by gigantic rocks. Generally, it is not too busy, and there's a chance of spotting stray penguins waddling past. The charming Seaforth restaurant with its wooden balcony overlooks the beach (see p25).

Bikini Beach, Strand
9 Less than an hour's drive east of Cape Town, secluded Bikini Beach is the most popular of the many beaches around Strand. Overlooked by the Helderberg Mountains, it offers clear views across False Bay. The shallow waters are safe for swimming, and an abundance of cafés and restaurants make it very popular with families. If the sunbathing gets monotonous, there are some great tidal rock pools at nearby Gordon's Bay. 🞝 Map D4

Bloubergstrand
10 The blouberg (blue mountain) referred to is Table Mountain (see pp18–19), whose flat-topped profile is displayed in full glory on a clear day. Sandy for the most part, Bloubergstrand has enough rocky protrusions to keep it interesting. Though rather exposed in windy weather, the beach is a favourite with water-sport enthusiasts (see p61).

Left **Golf course in Steenberg** Centre **Chiefs and Stormers rugby match** Right **Horseback riding**

🔟 Sports and Outdoor Activities

Rugby
Traditionally one of the world's top sides, the South African "Springboks" have twice won the Rugby World Cup (in 1995 and 2007). International matches are held at Newlands, home stadium of Western Province, Cape Town's provincial and super-14 side.

Football
Athlone Stadium on the Cape Flats is home to the Premium League Team Ajax Cape Town. The central Green Point Stadium has been rebuilt for the 2010 FIFA World Cup in South Africa. ◈ *Athlone Stadium: Map J1; (021) 637 6607 • Green Point Stadium: Map N1; (021) 434 4510*

Cricket
The Newlands Cricket Stadium is home to the Western Cape provincial side, which has produced several international players. At least one five-day test match and many One Day Internationals are played here every year. ◈ *Newlands Stadium: Map J2: (021) 657 2003*

Deep-Sea and Fly-Fishing
The waters off the Cape Peninsula are renowned for their great deep-sea fishing, with tuna being a speciality.

The mountain streams inland offer great fly-fishing opportunities. ◈ *Fly-fishing: Inkwazi: (021) 788 7611, www.inkwaziflyfishing.co.za; deep-sea trips: Big Blue Fishing Charters: (083) 777 1048*

Golfing
There are several golf courses in the Cape Town area. Two of the best are Rondebosch Golf Course and the Atlantic Beach Golf Estate. ◈ *Rondebosch Golf Course: Map B3; (021) 689 4176, Atlantic Beach: Map B2; (021) 553 2223*

Horse Riding, Noordhoek
The sandy Noordhoek Beach below Chapman's Peak is great for horse riding. Lessons are available for those over 14 years. ◈ *Sleepy Hollow Tours: (021) 789 2341; www.sleepyhollowhorseriding.co.za*

Mountain Biking
The mountainous winelands offer endless opportunities for keen cyclists and several

Surfing at a reef, Dungeon, off Cape Town

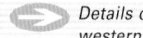 *Details of all golf courses are available on www.sa-venues.com/ western_cape_golf_courses.htm.*

Hikers atop Table Mountain

reserves have mountain-bike trails. Bikes can be hired in all the main centres, but the best agent for specialist riding trips is Langebaan's Live2ride. ⚲ *Live2ride: (082) 921 2301, www.live2ride.co.za*

8 Hiking in the Cape Fold Mountains

Hiking trails suitable for all levels of fitness traverse most of the nature reserves and national parks, offering an opportunity to explore the wildlife. Most can be walked unguided, but it's best to take along an experienced guide. ⚲ *Cape Eco-Tours: (021) 919 2282, www. cape-ecotours.co.za*

9 Surfing

The Western Cape offers some of the world's best surfing. The part of False Bay around Muizenberg is usually reliable, but busy in summer. Sites along the Atlantic seaboard are less busy and more challenging.

10 Kayaking and Canoeing in False Bay

Starting from Simon's Town, ideally on a windless day, paddle through scenic False Bay, and look for penguins, dolphins and whales. All first-timers can set out on calm days, but experienced adrenaline junkies prefer to kayak in stormy weather.

Top 10 South African Sporting Icons

1 Ernie Els
The former world number-one golfer, known as the Big Easy, has won three major titles.

2 Makhaya Ntini
South Africa's first black international cricketer reached number 2 in world rankings for test bowlers in 2006.

3 Benni McCarthy
His 29 international goals are a South African record he shares with fellow Capetonian footballer Shaun Bartlett.

4 Francois Pienaar
He captained the South African rugby team, which won the 1995 Rugby World Cup on their home turf.

5 Shaun Pollock
This former national cricket captain is a top-ranked bowling all-rounder (416 wickets/3,781 runs in tests).

6 Oscar Pistorius
Double-amputee world record holder at 100-m, 200-m and 400-m sprints.

7 Penny Heyns
An Olympic gold medallist who won the 100-m and 200-m breaststroke in 1996 – the first ever woman to achieve this amazing feat.

8 Roland Schoeman
Holder of three swimming world records and a member of the triumphant relay team at the 2004 Olympics.

9 Lucas Radebe
Former South Africa and Leeds captain, he played in the football team that won the 1996 Africa Nations Cup.

10 John Smit
Captain of the Springbok rugby team that won the 2007 Rugby World Cup.

 For a surfboard, try Muizenberg's Corner Surfshop on (021) 788 1191, or the Lifestyle Surf Shop on (021) 788 8218.

Left **Tourists exploring a cave** Right **Rock climbers at Table Mountain**

🔟 Adventure Activities

Paragliding
A spectacular location for paragliding, Cape Town and the surrounding winelands are best explored with a guide at first. Birdmen Paragliding offers day trips with radio contact, longer excursions from three days to a month, and introductory and full-licence courses. ✆ *Birdmen Paragliding: (082) 658 6710; www.birdmen.co.za*

Winelands Ballooning
A blissful way to start the day is to glide serenely over the beautiful winelands around Paarl in a hot-air balloon. Leave at sunrise, letting the wind navigate the balloon until you land, from where a support vehicle takes you for a champagne breakfast. ✆ *(021) 863 3192; runs Nov–Apr only, weather permitting; www.kapinfo.com*

Helicopter Rides
There is no more thrilling a way of seeing the Cape Peninsula and Table Mountain than from the air, when weather permits. You can charter a helicopter from the V&A Waterfront. ✆ *Base 4: (021) 418 4764; www.base4.co.za*

Caving
The network of sandstone caverns above Kalk Bay is reached via a rather steep footpath offering stunning

views over False Bay. The earliest evidence of human habitation at the Cape was excavated within these caves. It requires a bit of clambering and crawling to explore the cavernous depths properly. Be sure to carry a torch. ✆ *Quantum Adventures: (021) 789 0188; www.quantumadventures.co.za*

Scuba Diving
The coast to the north of Durban is renowned for its offshore reefs teeming with colourful fish. However, the chillier waters off Cape Town also provide great diving possibilities – immense forests of swaying kelp, friendly seals on the Atlantic seaboard, and a large number of shipwrecks everywhere. ✆ *Scuba Shack: (021) 785 6742; www.scubashack.co.za*

Quad Biking
About an hour's drive from Cape Town, the scenic Elgin Valley near Grabouw is a great site for quad biking. Passing

Paraglider launching off Lion's Head Mountain

Abseiling along the western face of Table Mountain

through forested slopes and *fynbos*-covered valleys, the guided and unguided trails can be undertaken as a day trip from Cape Town. ✆ *Kamazoo Quads: (072) 537 9310; www.kamazooquad.co.za*

River Rafting

The closest site for river rafting is the Breede River, which runs through the Robertson Valley lying to the northeast of Cape Town. Umkulu Safaris arrange day and overnight trips. They also run ambitious four- and six-day rafting trips on the Orange River along the border with Namibia. ✆ *Umkulu Trails: (021) 853 7952; www.umkulu.co.za*

Kloofing

One of the most popular activities out of Cape Town is to go *kloofing* – jumping into freshwater pools from cliffs up to 15 m (49 ft) high – in the Boland Mountains north of Cape Town. The best sites, including the ominously named Suicide Gorge, are reached after a fairly long hike. Not an activity for the unfit or the faint of heart! ✆ *Daytrippers: (021) 511 4766; www. daytrippers.co.za*

Abseiling

For spectacular heart-stopping views from Table Mountain, take in Abseil Africa's 112-m (367-ft) controlled descent of the western face. It is considered the world's highest commercial abseil. ✆ *Abseil Africa: (021) 424 4760; www.abseilafrica.co.za*

Rock Climbing

The craggy Western Cape peaks are a rock climber's paradise. City Rock is the leading centre to visit for a good selection of climbing gear or experienced instructors. It also has an indoor climbing centre. ✆ *City Rock: (021) 447 1326; call ahead to book a course; www.cityrock.co.za*

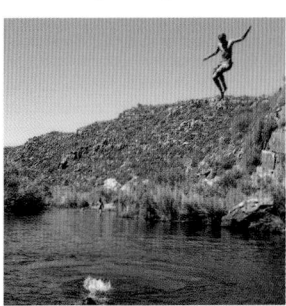

Kloofing, or jumping, into freshwater pools

 Abseiling is the process of descending from a fixed rope; the American term for it is rappelling.

Left **Bo-Kaap Museum** Right ***Litha*** **art depictions at the Red Shed Workshop**

🔟 Exploring Local Culture

1 District Six Museum

This emotionally charged museum is a testament to the iniquitous Group Areas Act passed by the National Party in the 1950s–60s. The museum focuses on day-to-day life in District Six before apartheid's bulldozers rumbled in *(see pp14–15)*.

2 Slave Lodge

This double-storey building opposite the Company's Garden was founded in 1679 as basic quarters for the wretched immigrants – the force behind the Cape's agricultural economy – who were imported from Malaysia and Indian Ocean islands. Now a museum, it charts the local and international history of the slave trade through a series of multimedia displays *(see pp8–9)*.

Display at Bo-Kaap Museum

3 Rock Art Gallery, South African Museum

South Africa is one of the world's most important repositories of rock art, with several sites dating back 10,000 years scattered through the country. The Rock Art Gallery has a superb display on this powerful prehistoric medium, including re-creations and an original panel relocated here to prevent damage by roadworks. 🌐 *Map P5 • 25 Queen Victoria St • (021) 481 3800 • Open 10am–5pm daily • Adm • www.iziko.org.za*

4 Langa

Founded in 1927, the oldest black township in Cape Town is also closest to the city centre. It was integral to the resistance to apartheid. Tours to Langa include the Tsoga Environmental Resource Centre and Gugu S'Thebe Arts Centre *(see p74)*.

5 Long Street

Affordable restaurants, quirky shops, tour operators and a smattering of gay-friendly nightspots line Long Street, one of the liveliest and most integrated parts of the city. Sleazy and trendy in equal parts, it is the hub of the city's backpacker scene *(see p63)*.

6 Red Shed Craft Workshop

This cavernous workshop has potters, candlemakers and other artisans at work. You can buy individualized handmade souvenirs or with enough notice, have special orders fulfilled. 🌐 *Map Q1 • The V&A Waterfront • www. waterfront.co.za*

Residents of Langa

Imizamo Yethu township

7 Meeting a Former Inmate at Robben Island

A trip to Robben Island ends with a tour of the high-security prison where anti-apartheid activists were incarcerated. With a former prisoner as your guide, get a first-hand account of time spent in South Africa's oldest political prison *(see pp12–13)*.

8 Khayelitsha

An isiXhosa phrase meaning "Our New Home", Khayelitsha, on the Cape Flats, started life in the 1950s after the Group Areas Act was passed. Recognized as a township only in 1985, it is one of South Africa's poorest urban centres *(see p74)*.

9 Bo-Kaap Museum

This museum explores the evolution of the Bo-Kaap *(see p62)* – an Islamic suburb inhabited by the Cape Malay people since the abolition of slavery in the 1830s. ⊛ *Map Q4 • 71 Wale St, Bo-Kaap • (021) 481 3939 • Open 10am–5pm daily • Adm • www.iziko.org.za*

10 Imizamo Yethu

A recent township, Imizamo Yethu is situated on the slopes above Hout Bay. The welcoming atmosphere makes up for the primitive conditions. Do not miss the tours provided by the residents *(see p78)*.

Top 10 Slang Words and Phrases

1 Ag!

Pronounced like the Scots "Och", this can be an expression of distaste (Ag, sis!), sympathy (Ag, shame!) or annoyance (Ag, no!).

2 Bru

Derived from the Afrikaans *broer* (brother), this is a generic term of male address, a bit like "dude" in the USA or "mate" in the UK.

3 Dop

An alcoholic beverage – or the act of drinking one (as in "let's have a quick dop").

4 Babalas

A colourful Cape Coloured term for a hangover.

5 Ek sé

Literally "I say", the phrase is used to prefix a statement or request in the same way.

6 Izzit?

Literally "Is it", this phrase is often interjected when another person speaks. It is similar to the English "really?"

7 Moerse

Very – as in "it's moerse cold" on a cold day.

8 Lekker

Good or nice (as in "we had a lekker time"). It can also mean tasty. Sweets (candies) are called *lekkers* in Afrikaans.

9 Just Now

This misleading phrase, which frequently confuses and amuses visitors to Cape Town, means "a bit later" – or "much later"!

10 Jol

The word means party or any good time, and is used both as a noun ("where's the jol?") or a verb ("let's jol").

Left **Belthazar Restaurant & Wine Bar** Right **Catharina's**

🔟 Wining and Dining

1 Belthazar Restaurant & Wine Bar

Former winner of the Best Steakhouse in South Africa, this popular restaurant on the V&A Waterfront is the place to go for a prime fillet or rump. More than 100 of the Cape's finest wines are available by the glass, while sought-after rare vintages are available by the bottle *(see p68)*.

2 Den Anker Restaurant and Bar

Set on a small jetty, this is one of the Waterfront's top eateries. It serves Belgian specialities, such as rabbit, fine wines and good Belgian beers. Eat outdoors with a view of seals and boats in the harbour. In poor weather, the boat-shaped bar compensates for being indoors *(see p68)*.

3 Africa Café

This eatery, renowned for its evening buffet of pan-African dishes, provides a "flying tour" of Africa's varied flavours. The lively bar is reason enough to linger after the buffet *(see p69)*.

Den Anker Restaurant and Bar

4 Savoy Cabbage

This is one of Cape Town's trendiest eateries, set in a restored Victorian building in the city centre. The historic setting is offset by a funky interior, and the imaginative menu is strong on game, shellfish and vegetarian dishes *(see p69)*.

5 Cape Malay Restaurant

Part of the Cellars-Hohenort Hotel and perhaps the city's finest traditional Cape restaurant, its daily-changing set menu is accompanied by choice Cape wines. The food is matched by gracious Cape Dutch architecture and the setting on an estate bordering the Kirstenbosch National Botanical Garden *(see p75)*.

6 Catharina's at Steenberg

Set below the majestic cliffs of Steenberg (Stone Mountain) this award-winning five-star restaurant, named after the estate's eccentric 17th-century founder, is housed in an airy Cape Dutch building. Strong on traditional Cape Malay dishes, it also serves a varied selection of creative meat and seafood dishes, complemented by a good wine list *(see p75)*.

7 Bon Appétit

Simon's Town's finest is a regular fixture in *Wine Magazine*'s "Top 100 South African Restaurants". This exceptional French restaurant, owned by a Michelin-trained

Bon Appétit

chef, is housed on the ground floor of the British Hotel. Delicious French food and good wine are served by candlelight. Set menu available *(see p81)*.

Volkskombuis
Something of a Stellenbosch institution, this proudly South African restaurant was founded on the north bank of the Eerste River in the 1970s. It continues to serve an excellent selection of local dishes, combining traditional recipes with adventurous contemporary touches *(see p90)*.

Le Quartier Francais
The ultimate culinary splash-out is the Tasting Room at Le Quartier Francais in central Franschhoek. Among the world's finest restaurants, it serves an eclectic selection of food and is anything but cheap. The stylish iCi Restaurant in the same building offers an affordable opportunity to sample the Le Quartier style *(see p91)*.

Le Pique Nique
Something about the Winelands invites lingering lawn picnics with chilled white wine. No estate offers this facility with as much panache as the Boschendal estate and its moderately pretentious Le Pique Nique, set below shady pines and blue mountains *(see p91)*.

Top 10 South African Dishes and Delicacies

1 Bobotie
A Cape Malay classic of minced beef and yellow rice, sweetened by raisins, and topped with an egg sauce.

2 Potjiekos
Meat and vegetable stew cooked slowly in a *potjie* (a small black pot) over an open fire.

3 Waterblommetjie Bredie
A Cape stew made of lamb and *waterblommetjie*, a water plant which resembles an artichoke.

4 Tomato Bredie
A thick, tasty tomato-based stew made of succulent Karoo lamb.

5 Boerewors
Spicy, fatty "Farmer's sausage", best *braaied* (barbecued) on an open fire.

6 Malva Pudding
This sweet, spongy Dutch pudding is made with apricots.

7 Melktert
This dish is a milkier and sweeter version of a custard tart. Dates back to Cape Malay-Dutch cooking.

8 Koeksister
Translated as "Cake sisters", this is a spiral pastry with a doughnut-like texture and a sticky-sweet coating.

9 Pap 'n' Stew
The traditional staple in most of South Africa, this is a meat stew that is eaten along with *mealie pap* (maize porridge).

10 Biltong
Spicy strips of dried, salted and spiced raw beef or game meat, biltong is reminiscent of beef jerky.

Cape Town & the Winelands' Top 10

For more restaurants and their price categories, see pp68, 75, 81, 90–91 and 99.

Ladysmith Black Mambazo performing at the Cape Town International Jazz Festival

Festivals and Events

Kaapse Klopse
Also known as the Cape Minstrel Festival, this colourful New Year's welcome originated as a response by former slaves to a 1848 visit by "blackfaces" (white American minstrels who blackened their faces with burnt cork). Local people paint their faces white and march through Cape Town. 🕾 1 Jan

Maynardville Open-Air Theatre
The 720-seat open-air theatre in Maynardville Park has hosted a Shakespeare-in-the-Park Festival since 1956, when *The Taming of the Shrew* was first performed here. It attracts up to 20,000 patrons annually. 🕾 Map I2 • Cnr of Church and Wolf Sts, Wynberg • (021) 421 7695 • Jan–Feb • www.maynardville. co.za

Cape Town Pride Festival
The city's most important gay festival was inaugurated in 2001. Pride Parade Day attracts a stream of colourful floats and involves drag shows, fashion events and an after party. Other events in the flamboyant fortnight-long festival include pageants, balls, tea parties and gay movies. 🕾 (021) 425 6463 • Feb–March • www.capetownpride.co.za

Cape Town Festival
Cape Town's most important arts festival began in 1999 to promote integration and celebrate the multi-racial

communities of Cape Town. It is held in April in The Company's Garden *(see pp8–9)*. 🕾 (021) 465 9042 • Apr • www.capetownfestival.co.za

Cape Town International Jazz Festival
South Africa's premier jazz event. Performers have included Gino Vannelli, Randy Crawford, Ladysmith Black Mambazo and Themba Mkhize. 🕾 (021) 422 5651 • Mar last weekend • www. capetownjazzfest.com

Stellenbosch Wine Festival
Wine-lovers descend on Stellenbosch for this four-day event that features more than 500 wines by over 100 Cape estates. The festival includes wine-tasting tutorials, craft workshops and kids' entertainment. 🕾 Map D2 • (021) 886 4310 • 31 Jul–3 Aug • www.wineroute.co.za

Hermanus Whale Festival
Late September is when Hermanus holds its annual whale festival. This week-long programme at Market Square

Kaapse Klopse

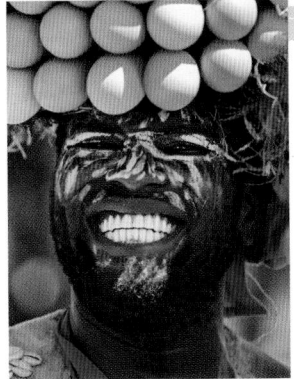

Eggman at the Hermanus Whale Festival

involves live music concerts, sporting events and sightings of the world's largest living creatures. 🐾 *Map U5* • *(028) 313 0928* • *Oct* • *www.whalefestival.co.za*

8 Cape Town International Comedy Festival

Inaugurated in 1997, this annual comedy festival featuring local and international comedians is held at several venues, including the Baxter, Artscape and Labia Theatres. 🐾 *(021) 425 6986* • *3 weeks in mid–Sep* • *www.comedyfestival.co.za*

9 Kirstenbosch Summer Sunset Concerts

A wonderful way to enjoy a Sunday sunset. The open-air concerts at the amphitheatre appeal to all musical tastes and are performed within the beautiful botanic gardens. 🐾 *Map H2* • *Rhodes Avenue, Newlands* • *(021) 761 2866*

10 Oude Libertas Summer Festival

This music festival at the historic Oude Libertas Estate on the Papagaaisberg has an eclectic programme, from chamber music to jazz and *boeremusiek* (Afrikaans folk). 🐾 *Stellenbosch* •*(021) 809 7473* • *Dec–Mar* • *www. oudelibertasamphitheatre.co.za*

Top 10 Local Things to Buy

1 Scarab Paper
Write on handmade writing paper produced from elephant dung using an ancient Chinese technique.

2 Ndebele Beadwork
A wide range of kaleidoscopic necklaces, bracelets and anklets from the Limpopo Province.

3 Zulu Basketry
The Zulu, South Africa's most populous ethnic group, are skilled weavers.

4 Swazi Candles
Multicoloured and interestingly shaped candles are produced in Swaziland and Mpumalanga.

5 Amarula
This creamy liqueur is produced from the endemic apricot-like marula fruit.

6 Music CDs
Any decent CD shop will stock a good selection of introductory CDs to the bustling local music scene.

7 Ostrich Leatherware
High-quality handbags are crafted from the hide of the world's largest bird.

8 Mohair Scarves and Shawls
Own an article that is made from what is reputed to be the world's finest and softest mohair.

9 Wine
Serious connoisseurs of wine can save a fortune by buying locally. Make arrangements in order to specially ship bottles home.

10 African Fine Arts
Many shops sell fine African masks, carvings and batiks, mostly from north of the Limpopo.

AROUND TOWN

CAPE TOWN & THE WINELANDS' TOP 10

Left **Main entrance, Castle of Good Hope** Right **A path through the Company's Garden**

Central Cape Town

T HE HISTORIC HEART OF SOUTH AFRICA'S *oldest city is bound by Table Bay to the north and Table Mountain to the south. Signal Hill forms an imposing barrier between the City Bowl's inner city suburbs and those along the Atlantic seaboard. The large number of historic buildings, excellent museums, cinemas, restaurants and nightclubs, together with a buzzing street life, confirm the city's status as one of Africa's major cultural centres. But the*

undoubted highlight, whether you are standing on the Castle of Good Hope's ramparts or nursing a chilled beer at a waterfront café, is Table Mountain, looming over the city centre with effortless majesty.

The façade of the evocative District Six Museum

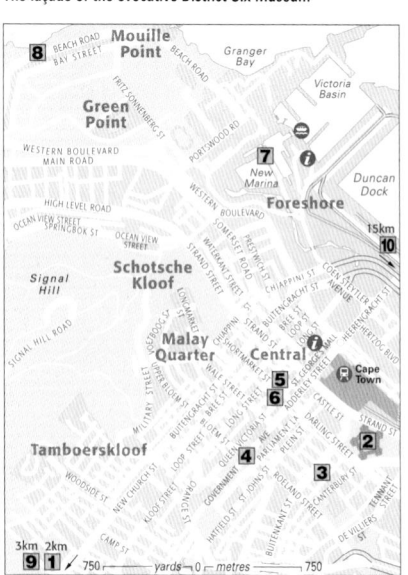

🔟 Sights

1. Table Mountain
2. Castle of Good Hope
3. District Six Museum
4. The Company's Garden
5. Greenmarket Square
6. Michaelis Collection
7. The V&A Waterfront
8. Beach Road
9. Camps Bay
10. Bloubergstrand

Preceding pages **The shores of Boulders Beach, Simon's Town**

Table Mountain

The 1,067-m (3,500-ft) high plateau of Table Mountain is reached by a rotating cablecar that offers 360° views across the city centre to the distant Hottentots Holland Mountains. At the top, a network of footpaths allows you to explore the *fynbos* vegetation and assorted wildlife. Maclear's Beacon, the highest summit, is less than an hour from the upper cableway. The adventurous traveller might like to undertake Abseil Africa's controlled 112-m (367-ft) descent from a ledge overlooking Camps Bay *(see pp18–19)*.

Castle of Good Hope

Constructed in 1666–79, Cape Town's oldest building now stands inland as a result of land reclamation, and still serves as the Western Cape's military headquarters. An imposing slate and sandstone pentagon, the rather utilitarian design is alleviated by the sculpted masonry on the bell tower and the Anton Anreith bas-relief above the Kat Balcony. An interesting military museum and the 19th-century William Fehr collection of art are also housed here *(see pp16–17)*.

District Six Museum

This moving tribute to District Six, bulldozed in the apartheid era *(see p34)*, is housed in the former Buitenkant Methodist Church, whose association with the anti-apartheid movement led to its forced closure in 1988. The museum's centrepiece is a vast, annotated floor map of the suburb in its multi-racial heyday. Other exhibits bear witness to the cruelty and destructiveness of the racism that dominated South African life for almost half a century *(see pp14–15)*.

The Company's Garden

Established in 1652 as a vegetable garden to provide fresh produce to Dutch East India Company (VOC) ships docking at Table Bay, the Company's Garden doubles as a botanical garden. At the heart of the so-called Museum Mile, this inner-city park, with a backdrop of Table Mountain, is a lovely spot for relaxing and strolling. You can spend a day exploring the buildings fronting its lawns, such as the Iziko Slave Lodge and the Iziko South African Museum and Planetarium *(see pp8–9)*.

Table Mountain cableway

Sign up for DK's email newsletter on traveldk.com

Around Town – Central Cape Town

Michaelis Collection

The Khoisan
When Van Riebeeck established Cape Town in 1652 *(see p35)*, the Western Cape had been inhabited by the Khoisan-speaking populace for several millennia. Within 200 years they were gone; some had fallen victim to diseases while others were killed by gun-toting settlers. Those who remained integrated into the mixed-race community, Cape Coloureds.

Greenmarket Square
This cobbled square in the heart of old Cape Town served as a slave market under the Dutch East India Company (VOC) *(see p34)*. Its name, however, alludes to a subsequent incarnation as a fruit and vegetable market that made way for a parking lot in the 1950s. Surrounded by historic buildings, many housing smart eateries and cafés, this graceful square is home to a popular pan-African craft market and an assortment of lively street performers juggling, dancing, singing or performing mimes.
S *Map Q4*

Michaelis Collection
This world renowned collection of paintings by Dutch and Flemish masters of the Golden Age (16th–18th centuries) was donated to the city by Sir Max Michaelis in 1914. Housed in the beautifully restored Old Townhouse, which served as the City Hall until 1905, the structure is counted among the foremost architectural gems of the city. It exemplifies the early Cape Rococo style with its graceful triple-arched portico and pretty belfry. S *Map P4*
• Greenmarket Square • (021) 481 3933
• Open 10am–5pm Mon–Fri, 10am–5pm Sat • Adm by donation • www.iziko.org.za

The V&A Waterfront
Cape Town's reconstituted harbour is also the city's foremost shopping venue. Literally hundreds of shops, ranging from bland chain stores to quirky craft stalls, can be found alongside several restaurants and a host of tourist spots, including the Nelson Mandela Gateway. Boat and helicopter operators offer harbour cruises and flights over Table Mountain *(see pp10–11)*.

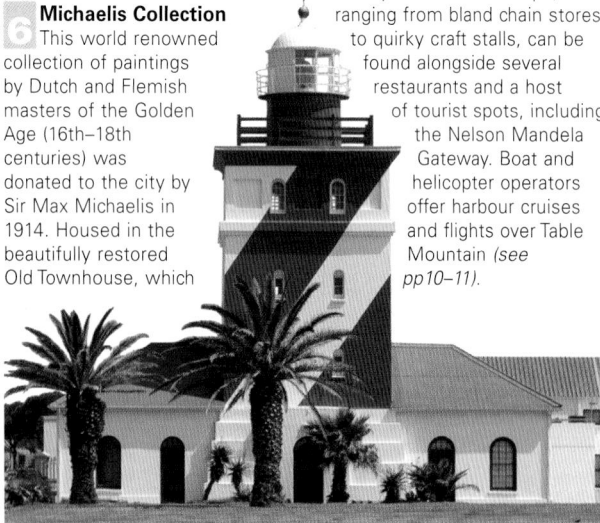

The Green Point Lighthouse, Beach Road

Waterfront buildings, Camps Bay

Beach Road

Passing through the suburbs of Green Point and Sea Point immediately west of the city centre, Beach Road runs along an attractive stretch of Atlantic coastline. The road is separated from the sea by a grassy promenade where locals jog, skateboard and walk their dogs. It's a great spot for some aimless wandering, especially at sunset. Also worth seeing is the Green Point Lighthouse, the oldest in the country. Map K3

Camps Bay

Wonderfully set between mountain and sea, Camps Bay is where suburban Cape Town's Atlantic seaboard gives way to the wild and unspoilt coastal scenery of the Cape Peninsula. This idyllic suburb boasts one of the nicest beaches in greater Cape Town and has a fine range of restaurants and bars situated on its waterfront. Map H1

Bloubergstrand

This long sandy beach 12 km (7 miles) north of the city centre offers the most spectacular view of Cape Town; Table Bay glittering in the foreground against a backdrop of Table Mountain in its flat-topped glory. The beach, though busy with locals in summer, is seldom crowded. There's a fair chance of spotting dolphins and whales in season in the chilly waters off the beach. Map B2

A Day in the City Centre

Morning

After breakfast, make your way to the **District Six Museum** (see pp14–15) and explore its stirring exhibits. Then walk a couple of blocks back down Buitenkant Road to the **Castle of Good Hope**, (see pp16–17) leaving time to admire the **City Hall** (see p17) where Mandela made his first public address after his release in 1990. At the castle, grab a snack at De Goeweneur Restaurant before joining one of the free guided tours that run daily at 11am. At noon, return to the main gate for the firing of the signal cannon. Either drop in at the castle's two museums or enjoy an early lunch at De Goeweneur. Then join the horse-drawn carriage tour of historic Cape Town that departs at 12:45pm and alight at **The Company's Garden** (see pp8–9).

Afternoon

If you didn't have lunch at the castle, there are plenty of choices here. When the weather's right for eating alfresco, **Gardens Tea Room** opposite the aviary has to be first choice. The atmospheric **Crypt Restaurant** in **St George's Cathedral** (see p8) is good on a gloomy day. Afterwards, take a stroll around the gardens, followed by a visit to one of the museums lining them, such as the **National Museum** and **Slave Lodge** (see p8). If you're feeling peckish, wander up to **Mount Nelson Hotel** (see p112) to sample its legendary tea buffet (2:30–5:30pm) before heading back to your hotel.

Left **Bo-Kaap** Centre **Star machine in the Planetarium** Right **South African Museum**

Best of the Rest

Planetarium
The centrally located Planetarium has daily shows introducing the dazzling southern sky – worthwhile for those heading into the Karoo, with its clear and brilliant night sky *(see p8)*.

St George's Mall
Running through the heart of the historic city centre, this pedestrian mall is usually abuzz with street musicians and busy market stalls. ✪ *Map Q4–Q5*

South African Museum
Mainly featuring natural history displays, the South African Museum also exhibits prehistoric rock art *(see p8)*.

South Africa Jewish Museum
Set in the country's oldest synagogue, this fascinating museum documents the history of South Africa's Jewish community. ✪ *Map P6 • Hatfield St • (021) 465 1546 • Open 10am–5pm Sun–Thu, 10am–2pm Fri • Adm • www.sajewishmuseum.co.za*

Bo-Kaap
The spiritual home of the Cape Malay community, Bo-Kaap (Upper Cape) is known for its colourfully painted houses. Its history is documented in the small Bo-Kaap museum *(see p51)*. ✪ *Map Q4*

Gold of Africa Museum
This museum documents the importance of gold in the economy of pre-colonial Africa. ✪ *Map P4 • 96 Strand St • (021) 405 1540 • Open 9:30am–5pm Mon–Sat • Adm • www.goldofafrica.com*

Signal Hill and Lion's Head
The climb or drive up Signal Hill is highly rewarding. Aim to be there at dusk for a view over the glittering city. ✪ *Map M3*

Clifton Beach
This is the closest of the four beaches to the city centre. It is popular on weekends and over holidays. ✪ *Map A2*

Association for the Visual Arts
Dedicated to the advancement of contemporary South African art, this gallery's exhibitions change every three weeks or so. ✪ *Map P4 • 35 Church St • (021) 424 7436 • Open 10am–5pm Mon–Fri, 10am–1pm Sat • www.ava.co.za*

Iziko Bertram House Museum
Restored in the early 1980s, this Georgian town house contains ten collections, including porcelain items and Georgian furniture. ✪ *Map P6 • Orange St • (021) 424 9381 • Open 10am–4:30pm Mon & Fri • www.iziko.org.za*

 To ensure safety, travel around Signal Hill and Lion's Head in a group.

Left **Ethnic jewellery from Greenmarket Square** Right **Victoria Wharf Mall, the V&A Waterfront**

🔟 Shops, Malls and Markets

1 The V&A Waterfront
The waterfront combines a wonderful harbourfront setting with a selection of shops and restaurants that is second to none *(see pp10–11)*.

2 Long Street
Those seeking a colourful shopping experience will enjoy Long Street's cult, craft and secondhand shops. ◈ *Map P5*

3 Pan African Market
This is an excellent place to check out crafts from all over Africa. Along with a cheerful café, you'll also find a hairdresser and tailor here. ◈ *Map P4 • 76 Long St • (021) 426 4478*

4 Greenmarket Square
Situated off Greenmarket Square, Cape Town's oldest flea market has a definite buzz about it. A variety of African crafts can be found alongside ethnically inspired clothing and jewellery *(see p60)*.

5 Cape Quarter
Cape Quarter has a historic location in the trendy De Waterkant suburb and houses shops specializing in crafts and jewellery. It also has several restaurants and cafés. ◈ *Map P3 • 72 Waterkant St • (021) 421 0737 • www.cape quarter.co.za*

6 Gardens Shopping Centre
This is the most popular shopping mall in the City Bowl, with a distinct boutique feel to many of its shops, though larger chains are also represented. ◈ *Map P6 • Mill St • (021) 465 1842*

7 Station Flea Market
The market stalls next to the station on Adderley Street Railway have a down-to-earth appeal, with items geared to the local market. ◈ *Map Q4*

8 Green Point Flea Market
This eclectic flea market is a good bet for shopping on Sundays, when other malls and markets tend to be quiet. ◈ *Map P2 • (021) 439 4805 • Open Sun only*

9 Canal Walk
Comparable in scale to the V&A Waterfront, this vast complex of shops, cinemas and restaurants is linked to the city by a shuttle bus from popular hotels. ◈ *Map R5 • (021) 555 4433 • www.canalwalk.co.za*

10 The Cape Gallery
Set in a historic building, this art gallery is probably the best place to buy works by a selection of local artists. ◈ *Map P4 • 60 Church St • (021) 423 5309 • Open 9:30am–5pm Mon–Fri, 10am–2pm Sat • www.capegallery.co.za*

When browsing in the markets, be alert and avoid carrying more cash than you are likely to need.

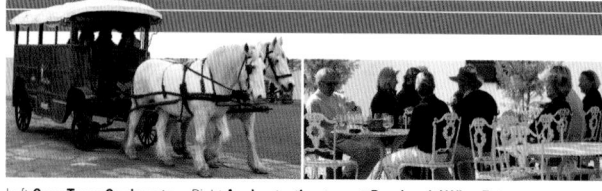

Left **Cape Town Carriage tour** Right **A wine-tasting tour at Boschendal Wine Estate**

🔟 Organized Activities & Day Tours

Cape Town Carriage
This horse-drawn carriage tours historic Cape Town, departing from the Castle of Good Hope and trotting to the Company's Garden and surrounding museums. ☎ *(021) 703 4396* • *Departures 10:30am, 12:45pm & 2:45pm*

Inverdoorn Game Reserve
This magnificent reserve is a 2.5-hour drive from Cape Town, in the stunning Karoo. Home to an abundance of wildlife, including White Rhino and a range of facilities and activities *(see p43)*.

Wine-Tasting Tour
The ideal way to enjoy wine-tasting is through the organized tours of the Winelands available out of Cape Town, Stellenbosch and Franschhoek *(see p106)*.

Cape of Good Hope Day Tour
Organized tours to magnificent Cape Point also take in the Boulders Penguin Colony and include stops along the Atlantic seaboard.

District Six and Townships Tour
A typical day tour starts with a visit to the District Six Museum, then moves on to the Langa and Khayelitsha townships, stopping for lunch at a local eatery or *shebeen* (bar). Zibonele Tours offer several variations. ☎ *(072) 740 1604* • *www.ziboneletours.co.za*

Robben Island
Probably the most popular organized excursion out of Cape Town is a guided tour of Robben Island, which includes the return boat trip from Nelson Mandela Gateway at the V&A Waterfront *(see pp12–13)*.

Whale and Dolphin Watching Cruise
Best undertaken in calm weather, cetacean-viewing excursions into Table Bay – though not as certain to produce whales as Hermanus – can be organized through kiosks lining the harbour at the V&A Waterfront.

Kloofing
Kloofing (literally "cliffing") is a popular local activity that involves leaping off cliffs into pools in mountain streams of the Winelands. Day trips entail a hike to the *kloofing* site *(see p49)*.

Table Bay Helicopter Trips
Several companies based at the V&A Waterfront offer thrilling helicopter trips with superb aerial views over Table Mountain and the city *(see p48)*.

Table Mountain Day Hike
Experienced hikers will enjoy the hiking possibilities offered at Table Mountain. They are best undertaken with a knowledge-able local guide to avoid being trapped by sudden weather changes. ☎ *Cape Eco-Tours* • *(021) 919 2282*

Several operators offer day tours; if your hotel can't recommend one, contact Day Trippers (021) 511 4766; www.daytrippers.co.za.

Left **Mitchell's Waterfront Brewery** Centre **Bascule Whisky and Wine Bar** Right **Café Manhattan**

🔟 Bars and Cafés

1 Jo'burg
One of Long Street's longest serving party spots, Jo'burg is popular for its foot-tapping music and affordable drinks. ⊗ *Map P5 • 218 Long St • (021) 442 0142*

2 Asoka
Located in an elegant Victorian town house, this stylish and intimate bar will tempt you with delicious cocktails and tasty tapas. ⊗ *Map N6 • 68 Kloof St • (021) 422 0909*

3 Fireman's Arms
A comfortable pub atmosphere with trestle tables inside and out, lots of beers and a simple menu. ⊗ *Map Q3 • cnr Buitengracht & Mechau Sts • (021) 419 1513*

4 Bascule Whisky and Wine Bar
South Africa's largest selection of whiskies, a good wine list, beer on tap and whisky-tasting evenings are the main draws of this waterfront bar. ⊗ *Map Q2 • Cape Grace, The V&A Waterfront • (021) 410 7083*

5 Ferryman's Tavern
Originally a Victorian warehouse, this tavern re-creates an English pub ambience and has beer on tap. You can sit outdoors on warm nights. ⊗ *Map P2 • The V&A Waterfront • (021) 419 7748*

6 Mitchell's Waterfront Brewery
In the same building as the Ferryman's Tavern, this pub produces one of South Africa's few privately brewed beers, Mitchell's Raven. ⊗ *Map P2 • The V&A Waterfront • (021) 418 4261*

7 Buena Vista Social Café
This Cuban-themed bar plays snappy salsa music and serves up a selection of local wines and imported spirits. ⊗ *Map N2 • 81 Main Rd, Green Pt • (021) 433 0611*

8 Neighbourhood Restaurant, Bar & Lounge
A great gastropub with a games room, large screens showing sporting events and a balcony overlooking Long Street. ⊗ *Map P4 • 163 Long Street • (021) 424 7260*

9 Café Manhattan
Triangular-shaped and painted a bright red, this café used to be the foremost venue of the area's gay scene. It remains a popular gay hangout, though not exclusively so. ⊗ *Map P3 • 74 Waterkant St • (021) 421 6666*

10 Nose Wine Bar
Cape Town's finest wine bar is owned by wine lovers who are expert at matching a bottle with your meal. It offers a selection of wines by the glass. ⊗ *Map P2 • 72 Waterkant St • (021) 425 2200*

Left **Musician at Mama Africa** Centre **Zula Sound Bar** Right **Roots**

🔟 Music Venues and Nightclubs

Mama Africa
Traditional music accompanies an excellent pan-African menu and lively contemporary African decor at this legendary bar and restaurant. 🌐 Map P5 • 178 Long St • (021) 426 1017

Zula Sound Bar
This Long Street favourite hosts live music most nights, with acts ranging from local and international rock to more relaxed acoustic sessions. 🌐 Map P5 • 194 Long St • (021) 424 2442 • www.zulabar.co.za

Roots
Reggae fans are particularly well-catered to at this chilled out venue, but it also hosts live music spanning various genres. 🌐 Map P5 • Lower Main Road, Observatory • (021) 448 7656

The Assembly
At the forefront of the city's underground music scene with a mix of local and international acts. 🌐 Map Q5 • 61 Harrington Street • (021) 465 7286

Green Dolphin Café
This waterfront jazz café is reputed to have hosted more successive nights of music than any such venue in the world. 🌐 Map P2 • The V&A waterfront • (021) 421 7471 • www.greendolphin.co.za

Marimba Restaurant
Part of the Cape Town International Conference Centre, this sophisticated restaurant sways to African jazz and world music. 🌐 Map Q3 • Cnr Coen Steyler & Heerengracht • (021) 418 3366 • www.marimbasa.com

Fiction DJ Bar and Lounge
Great local DJs create a vibrant atmosphere with different music nights Tuesday to Saturday. 🌐 Map P5 • 226 Long Street • (021) 424 5709

Chrome
Just off trendy Long Street, upmarket Chrome has a large dance floor and a VIP lounge aimed at older clubbers. 🌐 Map P5 • 6 Pepper St • (083) 700 6078 • www.chromect.com

Bronx
Bronx is Cape Town's best known gay bar. With a busy agenda of daily events, it attracts a varied party crowd. 🌐 Map P3 • 22 Somerset Rd, Green Point • (021) 419 9216 • www.bronx.co.za

Dizzy's Cigar Bar and Pub
Live bands play covers at this lively smoker-friendly venue. A DJ plays on after the band has finished its set. 🌐 Map N6 • 39 & 41 The Drive, Camps Bay • (021) 438 2686 • www.dizzys.co.za

Most of the listed music venues post details of upcoming live acts on their website.

Left **A performance at Artscape Theatre Centre** Right **An entertainment act at On Broadway**

TOP 10 Theatre and Entertainment

1 Artscape Theatre Centre
Cape Town's premier performing arts complex hosts ballet, opera and cabaret performances. ✪ Map R4 • DF Malan St • (021) 410 9800 • www.artscape.co.za

2 Labia Cinema
This art cinema, named after its benefactor, Count Labia, shows offbeat movies that are shunned by the mainstream. ✪ Map N6 • 68 Orange St • (021) 424 5927 • www.labia.co.za

3 Little Theatre Complex
The drama department of the University of Cape Town (UCT) stages its often experimental student productions at the Little Theatre. ✪ Map P6 • 37 Orange St • (021) 480 7129 • www.drama.uct.ac.za

4 Theatre in the District
An evening of Cape cuisine followed by a show about Cape Town providing an insight into life in the city all set in a converted church. ✪ Map R5 • 106 Chapel Street • (021) 686 2150

5 Cape Philharmonic Orchestra
Founded in 1914, South Africa's oldest professional symphony orchestra has a busy schedule. ✪ Map R4 • Artscape, DF Malan St • (021) 410 9809 • www.cpo.org.za

6 On Broadway
Drag acts, tongue-in-cheek cabaret and musicals are the mainstays of this gay supper venue. ✪ Map Q4 • 88 Shortmarket St • (021) 424 1194 • www.onbroadway. co.za

7 Theatre on the Bay
Stand-up comedy, musicals and conventional farces – often with a South African twist – are the staple of this theatre. ✪ Map G1 • 1A Link St, Camps Bay • (021) 438 3300 • www.theatreonthebay.co.za

8 Kirstenbosch Summer Sunset Concerts
Enjoy a picnic at sunset while listening to the open-air concerts (rock to big band) in the beautiful botanical gardens. ✪ Map H2 • Rhodes Avenue, Newlands • (021) 761 2866

9 Baxter Theatre
The Baxter has long been at the cutting edge of local theatre, particularly during the 1980s when it openly defied apartheid laws. ✪ Map J1 • (021) 680 3989 • Main Rd, Rondebosch • www.baxter.co.za

10 Evita se Perron
This supper club in Darling has been named after Evita Bezuidenhout, a South African equivalent of Dame Edna Everage created by satirist, Pieter-Dirk Uys. ✪ Map T3 • Darling • (022) 492 2851 • www.evita.co.za

Left **221 Waterfront** Centre **Den Anker Restaurant & Bar** Right **Belthazar Restaurant & Wine Bar**

Eateries at the V&A Waterfront

Willoughby & Co
Seafood is the speciality at this informal venue on Victoria Wharf. It is particularly notable for its sushi and the selection of wines by the glass. ✪ *Map Q1 • (021) 418 6115 • RRR*

221 Waterfront
Every table has a stunning view in this multi-level, achingly stylish restaurant offering incredible international, fusion cuisine. It also has a cocktail lounge. ✪ *Map Q1 • Upper Level, Victoria Wharf • (021) 418 3633 • RRR*

Sevruga
A large and varied menu, of good quality dishes and an extensive wine list of mainly local producers. The staff are often too relaxed but always friendly. ✪ *Map Q5 • Shop 4, Quay 5 • (021) 421 5134 • RRRR*

Baia Seafood Restaurant
This brightly decorated restaurant serves top-notch sea-food and meat dishes, best enjoyed from the balcony with its fine views of Table Mountain. ✪ *Map Q1 • (021) 421 0935 • RRRRR*

Den Anker Restaurant and Bar
This stands out from the crowd for its great seafront location and high-ceilinged interior. Belgian specialities such as mussels, rabbit and Belgian beer are served. ✪ *Map P2 • (021) 419 0249 • RRRR*

Belthazar Restaurant & Wine Bar
Belthazar is a multiple award-winning steakhouse specializing in meat and poultry and claims to have the world's longest by-the-glass wine list. ✪ *Map Q1 • (021) 421 3753 • RRRRR*

Green Dolphin Café
Adventurous meat and seafood dishes with varied influences sit alongside a great wine list at this café, which also hosts nightly jazz shows. There is optional outdoor seating. ✪ *Map P2 • (021) 421 7471 • RRRRR*

Vida e Caffé
This café's stated claim to serve the best coffee on the planet has considerable merit, as does the varied selection of pastries and other accompaniments. ✪ *Map Q1 • (021) 425 9440 • R*

Harrie's Pancakes
Renowned for savoury and sweet filled pancakes, this well-liked lunchtime spot is conveniently located alongside the Nelson Mandela Gateway *(see p9)* to Robben Island. ✪ *Map Q2 • (021) 421 0887 • R*

Rooti's Cape Malay Restaurant
Unpretentious decor, a good selection of Cape Malay favourites and other spicy local dishes make this a popular lunchtime hang out. ✪ *Map Q2 • (021) 425 8810 • R*

Price Categories

For a three-course meal for one, including half a bottle of wine, cover charge, taxes and extra charges.

R	under R150
RR	R150–200
RRR	R200–250
RRRR	R250–300
RRRRR	over R300

Savoy Cabbage

⬆10 Restaurants

1 The Cape Colony
Set in the Mount Nelson Hotel *(see p112)*, this award-winning restaurant has a changing menu of South African dishes with a strong Asian influence. ◈ *Map P6 • 76 Orange St • (021) 483 1948 • RRRRR*

2 Savoy Cabbage
A historic setting, funky interior and imaginative menu make Savoy Cabbage one of Cape Town's hottest eateries. ◈ *Map P4 • 101 Hout St • (021) 424 2626 • RRRRR*

3 Aubergine Restaurant
This chic restaurant serves seafood prepared with a fusion of African, Asian and European influences. ◈ *Map P6 • 39 Barnet St, Gardens • (021) 465 4909 • RRRRR*

4 Bukhara
Cape Town's top Indian restaurant has an extensive menu that includes a varied vegetarian selection. ◈ *Map Q4 • 33 Church St • (021) 424 0000 • RRRRR*

5 Millers Thumb
This is a casually trendy spot with wooden floors, an eye-catching decor and a changeable menu chalked on a blackboard. It serves Cajun/Creole seafood. ◈ *Map N6 • Kloof Nek Road, Tamberskloof • (021) 424 3838 • RR*

6 Africa Café
A nightly buffet of pan-African dishes make this an excellent option for sampling the varied flavours of the continent. ◈ *Map P4 • 108 Shortmarket St • (021) 422 0221 • Open for dinner only • RRRR*

7 Chef Pon's Asian Kitchen
Unpretentious and affordable, Cape Town's most extensive Asian menu includes dishes from Japan and China to India and Mongolia. ◈ *Map P6 • 12 Mill St, Gardens • (021) 465 5846 • RR*

8 Caveau
Located in historic Heritage Square you can enjoy the seasonally inspired food at outside tables. Huge selection of wines. ◈ *Map P4 • Heritage Sq, 92 Bree St • (021) 422 1367 • RRRR*

9 Blues
A fixture on Camps Bay for 15 years, this perennial favourite has an adventurous menu of Italian-influenced seafood and meat dishes. ◈ *Map N6 • The Promenade, Victoria Rd, Camps Bay • (021) 438 2040 • RRRR*

10 Societi Bistro
A great favourite with locals and visitors with an enticing menu, including local seasonal produce, of exceptional value. ◈ *Map P6 • 50 Orange St, Gardens • (021) 424 2100 • RRR*

Left **Steenberg Wine Estate** Right **Shacks fronting new buildings at Langa Township**

Southern Suburbs

CAPE TOWN'S MOST SIGNIFICANT CLUSTER *of suburban attractions lies amidst the prestigious belt of leafy residential property that stretches southward from the city centre, flanked to the west by Table Mountain and to the east by the incongruously poor Cape Flats. An area of interest for nature lovers, Kirstenbosch and Tokai offer scenic surroundings for a stroll. The*

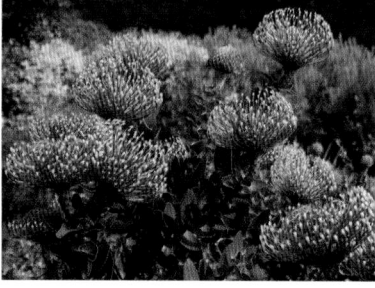

Protea blooms at Kirstenbosch National Botanical Garden

estates along the Constantia Wine Route are as enjoyable as its more far-flung counterparts around Stellenbosch. For art lovers, the Irma Stern Museum is a cultural highlight, while sports fans can take in a rugby or cricket match at the world-class Newlands Stadia.

10 Sights

1. Rhodes Memorial
2. Irma Stern Museum
3. Newlands Rugby Stadium and Cricket Ground
4. Kirstenbosch National Botanical Garden
5. Groot Constantia
6. Klein Constantia
7. Tokai Forest and Arboretum
8. Steenberg Wine Estate
9. Buitenverwachting Wine Estate
10. Cape Flats Townships

Preceding pages **Kirstenbosch National Botanical Garden**

Rhodes Memorial

Rhodes Memorial

One-time prime minister of the Cape and founder of the Rhodesias (now Zimbabwe and Zambia) *(see p35)*, CJ Rhodes has a memorial dedicated to him on a lookout point below Devil's Peak, which offers memorable views across the Cape Flats. The monument has Neo-Classical aspirations with its Doric columns and stone lions modelled on Nelson's Column. ◉ *Map H1 • (021) 689 9151 • Restaurant: open 9am– 5pm daily • www.rhodesmemorial.co.za*

Irma Stern Museum

This underrated museum opened in 1971 in the house where versatile artist Irma Stern lived till her death in 1966. Trained in Germany, Stern's impressionist portraits gained international acclaim, but her idealized rendition of African subjects provoked controversy at home. As well as her paintings, the museum also houses Stern's collection of Africana, notably an early 20th-century Congolese stool. ◉ *Map H1 • Cecil Rd, Rosebank • (021) 685 5686 • Open 10am–5pm Tue–Sat • Adm • www. irmastern.co.za*

Newlands Rugby Stadium and Cricket Ground

Newlands hosted its first inter-national rugby test in 1891. A multipurpose venue with a crowd capacity of 51,100, it is home to one of South Africa's Super 14 rugby teams *(see p46)*. Nearby, towering Table Mountain looms over the scenic Newlands Cricket Ground. ◉ *Map J2*

Kirstenbosch National Botanical Garden

South Africa's most beautiful botanical garden extends up to the eastern slopes of Table Mountain. It boasts a rich selection of flora and birdlife typical to the Western Cape. The network of wide footpaths, suitable for wheelchair users, forms a spring-board for visitors to explore the *fynbos*-draped upper slopes of Table Mountain *(see pp20–21)*.

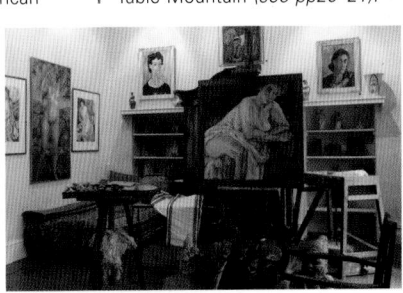

The studio at Irma Stern Museum

Groot Constantia Estate

South Africa's oldest wine estate is situated in the suburb of Constantia, below the eastern contours of Table Mountain. The opportunity to taste the award-winning wines alone justifies a visit, as does the stately Manor House *(see pp22–3)*.

Manor House Museum in Groot Constantia

Klein Constantia Estate

A subdivision of the original Van der Stel estate, Klein Constantia is arguably the finest wine producer in Constantia. Of note is the Vin de Constance, a re-creation of the natural, sweet dessert wine whose ancestral namesake was a favourite with Napoleon Bonaparte. ◈ *Map H2*
• *Klein Constantia Rd* • *(021) 794 5188*
• *Tasting: 9am–5pm Mon–Fri, 9am–1pm Sat* • *www.kleinconstantia.com*

Tokai Forest and Arboretum

Incorporated into Table Mountain National Park, this pine and eucalyptus plantation encloses a Victorian arboretum, which has native forests. Popular with birdwatchers, its winged residents include the forest buzzard and Verreaux's eagle. ◈ *Map H3*
• *Tokai Rd, Tokai* • *(021) 428 9111* • *Open 8am–5pm daily* • *Adm* • *www.sanparks.org*

Steenberg Wine Estate

Located on the oldest farm in the Constantia Valley and set below the eponymous "Stone

Buitenverwachting Wine Estate

Mountain", Steenberg was established in 1682 as Swaaneweide by Catharina Ras. Its award-winning wines are headed by a superb Sauvignon Blanc reserve and a red blend bearing Catharina's name. The estate has a golf course attached. ◈ *Map H3*
• *Steenberg Rd* • *(021) 713 2211* • *Tasting: 9:30am–4:30pm Mon–Fri, 10am–4pm Sat & Sun; cellar tours: call ahead* • *www.steenberg-vineyards.co.za*

Buitenverwachting Wine Estate

Translated as "Beyond Expectations"– an allusion to the 100-tonne grape harvest reaped by Ryk Cloete in 1825 – this 18th-century Cape Dutch homestead is set at the foot of Constantia Mountain. Though the flagship wine is a Bordeaux-style blend, (Christine), the estate also produces unblended reds and whites. There is a restaurant on-site. ◈ *Map H3* • *Klein Constantia Rd, Constantia* • *(021) 794 5190* • *Tasting 9am–5pm Mon–Fri, 9am–1pm Sat*
• *www.buitenverwachting.co.za*

Cape Flats Townships

Practically uninhabited until the 1940s, the sandy flats on the east of the peninsula were urbanized after forced relocation of locals from "Whites Only" suburbs to townships such as Khayelitsha, Langa and Gugulethu. Despite upliftment, poverty is still high. ◈ *Map I1*

Simon's Restaurant, Groot Constantia Estate

Price Categories

For a three course meal for one, including half a bottle of wine, cover charge, taxes and extra charges.

R	under R150
RR	R150–200
RRR	R200–250
RRRR	R250–300
RRRRR	over R300

🔟 Restaurants

Boer & Brit Pub
1 Set on an 18th-century estate, this drinking hole has a sensibly priced menu and a balcony for lunches in summer. ◎ *Map H2 • Alphen Hotel, Alphen Dr, Constantia • (021) 794 5011 • RR*

Cape Malay Restaurant
2 Cape Town's leading purveyor of spicy Cape Malay cuisine is situated in the historic Cellars-Hohenort Hotel. ◎ *Map H2 • 93 Brommersvlei Rd, Constantia • (021) 794 2137 • RRRR*

Jonkershuis Restaurant
3 This cosy favourite set on Groot Constantia offers a Cape Malay menu. Unusually, lunch is pricier than the well-priced evening buffets. ◎ *Map H2 • Groot Constantia • (021) 794 6255 • RRR*

Simon's Restaurant
4 A contemporary restaurant on Groot Constantia, Simon's Restaurant is renowned for its steaks and seafood. A selection of affordable sandwiches caters to children. ◎ *Map H2 • Groot Constantia • (021) 794 1143 • RRRR*

Buitenverwachting Restaurant
5 A multiple award-winning Winelands restaurant with an inventive menu that combines continental and local influences. Sumptuous picnic baskets are available at a café on the estate. ◎ *Map H2 • Buitenverwachting Klein Constantia Rd • (021) 794 3522 • RRRRR*

Pastis Brasserie
6 This outdoor-oriented eatery serves French cuisine, as well as filled baguettes and a selection of pub food. ◎ *Map H2 • High Constantia Centre, Constantia Main Rd, Constantia • (021) 794 8334 • RRR*

Silvertree Restaurant
7 Conveniently located in the Kirstenbosch National Botanical Garden, Silvertree's menu is supplemented by filled pancakes and sandwiches. Picnic baskets are also available *(see p20).*

Constantia Uitsig Restaurant
8 Set on the Uitsig Wine Estate, this restaurant matches a variety of South African and Italian dishes with the estate's acclaimed wines. ◎ *Map H2 • Constantia Uitsig Estate, Spaanschemat River Rd • (021) 794 4480 • RRRRR*

La Colombe
9 This Uitsig institution in an airy Cape Dutch building serves superlative French and fusion cuisine and top-notch Cape and French wines. ◎ *Map H2 • Constantia Uitsig Estate, Spaanschemat River Rd • (021) 794 2390 • RRRRR*

Catharina's at Steenberg
10 Housed in spacious rooms in a 17th-century Cape Dutch building, this five-star restaurant on Steenberg Estate serves seafood and Cape Malay dishes. ◎ *Map H3 • Steenberg Estate, Steenberg Rd, Tokai • (021) 713 2222 • RRRRR*

For more restaurants in and around Cape Town, see pp52–3, 81, 90–91, 99.

Left **Fishing boats at Hout Bay harbour** Right **Hout Bay as seen from Chapman's Peak Drive**

The Cape Peninsula

THE CAPE PENINSULA IS A MOUNTAINOUS SLIVER OF LAND *that extends southward from Cape Town to Cape Point, flanked by the open Atlantic to the west and False Bay to the east. Two-thirds of the coastline along the north of the peninsula is studded with quaint villages, sandy beaches and pretty seaside resorts. However, the ragged mountain spine remains largely unsettled, supporting a cover of unspoilt fynbos interspersed with plantation forest. Most of the peninsula is protected within Table Mountain National Park (TMNP). Outdoor enthusiasts living in Cape Town will testify to the opportunities that TMNP presents; you could spend a lifetime exploring this scenic tract of land, but for time-bound tourists, highlights in the peninsula include the Cape of Good Hope sector of TMNP (see pp26–7), the entertaining penguin colony residents at Boulders Beach near Simon's Town, and the lovely beaches at Muizenberg, Noordhoek and Fish Hoek.*

Scarlet Ibis at World of Birds

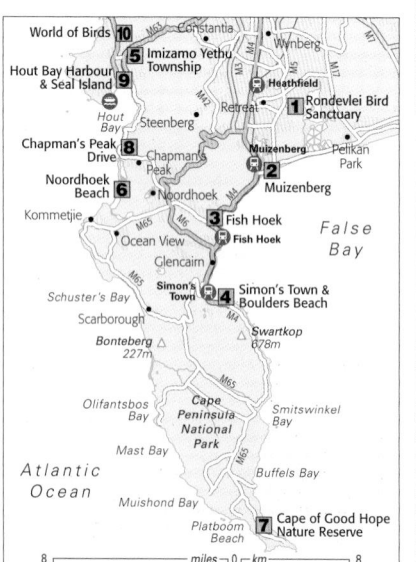

Sights

1. Rondevlei Bird Sanctuary
2. Muizenberg
3. Fish Hoek
4. Simon's Town and Boulders Beach
5. Imizamo Yethu Township
6. Noordhoek Beach
7. Cape of Good Hope Nature Reserve
8. Chapman's Peak Drive
9. Hout Bay Harbour and Seal Island
10. World of Birds

Sunbathers at Fish Hoek beach

Rondevlei Bird Sanctuary

A short drive north of Muizenberg, Rondevlei – Cape Town's best bird sanctuary – is home to 230 marine and fresh-water species, which can be glimpsed from the short walking trail that connects its hides. Grebes, rails, herons and gulls are well represented here. Hippos were introduced in 1982 to control the spread of surface vegetation. *Map J3 • 1 Fisherman's Walk, Rondevlei • (021) 706 2404 • Open 7:30am–5pm daily; Dec–Feb 7:30am–7pm daily • Adm • www.rondevlei.co.za*

Muizenberg

This resort town on False Bay was the location chosen a century ago by Witwatersrand gold magnates to build a row of seafront mansions. Though less prestigious now, the town's historical sights include Het Posthuys, built as a tollhouse in 1742, the battlements, which are remnants of the 1795 Anglo-Dutch Battle of Muizenberg, the Edwardian railway station and Rhodes Cottage Museum, where CJ Rhodes died in 1902. The wide, sheltered beach is a haven for surfers and swimmers. *Map J3*

Fish Hoek

The quaint village of Fish Hoek lies at the mouth of the Silvermine River between Muizenberg and Simon's Town, and boasts one of the warmest and safest swimming beaches on the Peninsula. The clifftop Jager's Path runs southward from town and offers good vantage points for whale watching. Overlooking the town is Peers Cave, one of the Cape's most important archaeological sites and a national monument. It contains evidence of human occupation dating back 11,000 years. *Map H4*

Simon's Town and Boulders Beach

A naval base for over 200 years, the pleasantly time-warped feel of Simon's Town is enhanced by the "Historic Mile", a row of Victorian façades lining St George Street. The town's Victorian railway station is the southern terminus of one of the world's great suburban train rides. The route follows the False Bay seafront back to Muizenberg. The penguin colony south of the town centre at Boulders Beach is the main attraction *(see pp24–5).*

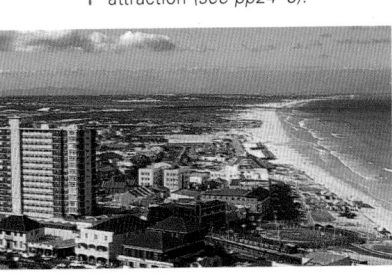

Muizenberg's beachfront

Cape Floral Kingdom

The smallest of the world's six floral kingdoms, the Cape consists of a unique floral community known as *fynbos* ("fine bush") a reference to the narrow leaves of many plants. A UNESCO World Heritage Site and a biodiversity hotspot for its floral wealth, the Cape Peninsula supports more indigenous species than the entire British Isles.

Shacks on the mountainside, Imizamo Yethu

Imizamo Yethu Township

This name is an isiXhosa phrase meaning "Through Collective Struggle". This small township was established on the outskirts of Hout Bay after the collapse of apartheid in the 1990s. The township's picturesque setting overlooking the harbour is offset in shocking contrast by the harsh living conditions endured by its 14,000 residents. Township Tours SA provides tours into Imizamo Yethu. ◈ *Map G2 • Township Tours SA: (083) 719 4870; 10:30am, 1pm, 4pm daily*

Noordhoek Beach

An expanse of bone-white sand running from the base of Chapman's Peak to Kommetjie,

The shores of Noordhoek Beach

Noordhoek is the most beautiful beach on the Cape Peninsula. It is a lovely spot for walks and birdwatching; you may even catch a glimpse of the endangered black oystercatcher. Horse riding is also on offer here *(see p46)*. ◈ *Map G3*

Cape of Good Hope Nature Reserve

This reserve is the scenic highlight of the Peninsula, dotted with stunning viewpoints such as Rooikrans, Gifkommetjie and Cape Point. It is an important stronghold for the Cape's unique *fynbos* habitat and for wildlife such as the eland and the endemic bontebok *(see pp26–7)*.

Chapman's Peak Drive

Named after the peak that soars above it, Chapman's Peak Drive, constructed in 1915–22, is a magnificent stretch of road. Excavated into a band of soft shale in the almost-vertical cliff face that connects Hout Bay to Noordhoek, the road runs past parking spots from where you can watch the Atlantic batter the cliff's base. It now operates as a toll road after years of repair work. ◈ *Map G3*

9 Hout Bay Harbour and Seal Island

Hout Bay's busy little harbour is the launching point for boat trips to Seal Island, a flat granite outcrop that lies about 6 km (4 miles) offshore. The island's rocky shores support up to 75,000 Cape fur seals, the largest colony in South Africa. People are forbidden from landing on the island, but plenty of seals can be seen from the boat, together with various marine birds including black oystercatchers, African penguins and breeding colonies of three different cormorant species. ◈ Map G3 • Hout Bay • Tours every hour

Reposing seals on Seal Island

10 World of Birds

In a leafy suburb of Hout Bay, the World of Birds houses around 400 species, from indigenous garden birds such as bulbuls and parrots, to spectacular exotic species such as the scarlet ibis and Indian peacock. It also has an important breeding programme for the endangered southern bald ibis and crowned crane. The Monkey Jungle is home to marmosets, tamarins and squirrel monkeys from South America, as well as a charismatic meerkat family and the Malagasy hedgehog tenrec. ◈ Map G2 • Valley Rd, Hout Bay • (021) 790 2730 • Adm • www.worldofbirds.org.za

A Full-Day Driving Tour to Cape Point

Morning

After an early breakfast, head down the Atlantic seaboard via Camps Bay. Leave in time to break the 45-minute drive to **Hout Bay** with stops along **Chapman's Peak Drive** to enjoy the view. If you reach Hout Bay before 9:30am, hop aboard a round-trip cruise to **Seal Island**. Then continue your journey, driving south to the **Cape of Good Hope** sector of **Table Mountain National Park** (see p40). Stop at the Buffelsfontein Visitor Centre before you reach the Cape Point car park. If you're already peckish, enjoy a scenic lunch at the **Two Oceans Restaurant** (see p81) overlooking False Bay, or wait until after you've climbed the steep footpath (or caught the funicular) to **Cape Point Lighthouse** (see p27).

Afternoon

Walk off the lunch following the footpath from the car park to the Cape of Good Hope Beach, or drive back along the main road through the reserve towards the entrance gate, diverting to the **Rooikrans**, **Gifkommetjie** and **Platboom Beach**. Leave by 3pm, following the road that hugs the False Bay seaboard towards **Simon's Town** (see p76). Stop occasionally to look out for whales. Before you reach Simon's Town, turn right for **Boulders Beach**, (see p76) to watch the squabbling penguins. Before driving back, enjoy a drink at **Seaforth Restaurant** (see p81), or at **Bertha's** (see p81), overlooking Simon's Town's harbour.

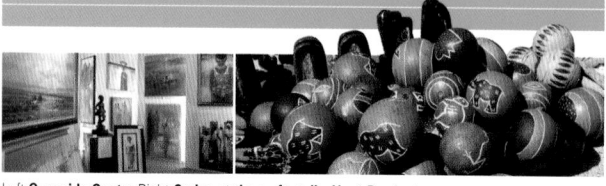

Left **Quayside Centre** Right **Curios at the craft stalls, Hout Bay harbour**

🔟 Galleries and Shops

1 Kalk Bay Gallery
This gallery specializes in fine art by local artists. You can have your purchase shipped to anywhere in the world. 🗺 Map H4
• 62 Main Rd, Kalk Bay • (021) 788 1674

2 Artvark
A pioneer of a unique style of silver, copper and brass cutlery, this shop also sells hand-crafted metal jewellery. 🗺 Map H4
• 48 Main Rd, Kalk Bay • (021) 788 5584

3 Quagga Art and Books
This highly regarded anti-quarian bookshop has numerous out-of-print titles. 🗺 Map H4
• 86 Main Rd, Kalk Bay • (021) 788 2752

4 Kalk Bay Modern
Local modern art, textiles and crafts are featured in this gallery. 🗺 Map H4 • Windsor House, 150 Main Rd, Kalk Bay • (021) 788 6571

5 Quayside Centre
A multi-storey complex below Quayside Hotel, the centre boasts curio shops, a book shop, and eateries overlooking Simon's Town's harbour. 🗺 Map H4

A sculpture display at Kalk Bay Modern

6 Sophea Gallery
This Buddhist influenced set-up consists of a gallery for local art, a Tibetan Teahouse serving vegetarian food and a sanctuary for meditation. 🗺 Map H4 • 2 Harrington Rd, Seaforth • (021) 786 1544

7 Longbeach Mall
The peninsula's largest shopping complex contains more than 100 shops including super-markets, a multi-screen cinema, a craft market, restaurants and coffee shops. 🗺 Map H3 • Cnr Buller Louw & Sunnydale Rd, Noordhoek
• (021) 785 5955

8 Ethno Bongo
The frames, candle-holders and fabulous handmade jewellery crafted from seashells, feathers and ostrich eggshells at this quality gift shop make good gifts to take home. 🗺 Map G2 • Main Rd, Hout Bay • (021) 790 0802

9 Hout Bay Harbour Craft Market
A row of stalls in Hout Bay harbour sell local curios, ranging from batiks to beadwork and wooden carvings. 🗺 Map G3

10 Rose Korber Art
This renowned art dealer has a collection of works by contemporary South African artists. Korber also curates an annual exhibition of top contemporary South African art. 🗺 Map H1 • 48 Sedgemoor Rd, Camps Bay • (021) 438 9152

Price Categories

For a three course meal for one, including half a bottle of wine, cover charge, taxes and extra charges.

R	under R150
RR	R150–200
RRR	R200–250
RRRR	R250–300
RRRRR	over R300

Bertha's restaurant

TOP 10 Restaurants

1 Olive Station

This unique restaurant and delicatessen specializes in Levantine and Mediterranean dishes, served *mezze* style in the courtyard. ⚲ *Map I3 • 165 Main Rd, Rondebosch • (021) 686 8224 • Closed Sun and for dinner • RR*

2 Galley Restaurant

Also known as the Bayside, this beachfront eatery serves up fresh seafood – the mixed platters are legendary – and a good selection of meat dishes. ⚲ *Map H4 • Fish Hoek Beach • (021) 782 3354 • RR*

3 Bertha's

With an attractive location on the Quayside Centre's ground floor, Bertha's serves meat and seafood at good value. ⚲ *Map H4 • Simon's Town Harbour • (021) 786 2138 • RR*

4 Bon Appétit

Visit this French restaurant, with a historic setting below the British Hotel, for the best up-market dining experience on the False Bay seaboard. ⚲ *Map H4 • 90 St George's St, Simon's Town • (021) 786 2412 • RRRR*

5 Seaforth Restaurant

Ideally combined with a visit to the Boulders penguin colony (see p77), this seafood restaurant also serves excellent pasta and pizza dishes. ⚲ *Map H4 • Seaforth Beach, Boulders • (021) 786 4810 • RR*

6 Two Oceans Restaurant and Snack Bar

The only restaurant at Cape Point is notable for its staggering view across False Bay. A shop next door sells take-away fare such as burgers and sandwiches. ⚲ *Map I6 • Cape Point • (021) 780 9200 • Closed for dinner • RRRR*

7 Cape Point Ostrich Farm

Lying at the entrance gate to Cape of Good Hope Nature Reserve, this farm restaurant serves delicious ostrich platters. ⚲ *Map H6 • (021) 780 9294 • RRR*

8 Lookout Deck

Great harbour views are a feature of this popular restaurant. It serves great seafood platters and affordable snacks. ⚲ *Map G3 • Hout Bay Harbour • (021) 790 0900 • RR*

9 Suikerbossie Restaurant

This isolated 1940s banquet hall on *suikerbos-* (sugar bush-) covered slopes serves an à la carte menu during the week and a buffet on weekends. ⚲ *Map G2 • Hout Bay-Llandudno Rd • (021) 790 1450 • Closed Mon; Sun: Book ahead • RRR*

10 Azure Restaurant

Set in the prestigious Twelve Apostles Hotel (see p112) south of Camps Bay, this gourmet restaurant uses *fynbos* plants as herbs, and combines Cape cuisine with international elements. ⚲ *Map H1 • Victoria Rd, Camps Bay • (021) 437 9000 • RRRRR*

Restaurants are open for lunch as well as dinner unless otherwise noted.

Left **Historic house in Stellenbosch** Right **An adult cheetah at Spier Wine Farm**

The Winelands

THE MOUNTAINOUS TERRITORY *immediately inland of Cape Town, often referred to as the Boland (literally "Uplands"), is among the most beautiful parts of South Africa. Its rugged sandstone peaks, interspersed with lush well-watered valleys, support intensive cultivation of deciduous fruit and trees. This region also forms the heart of the country's wine industry; it is home to around 300 different wineries and is well organized for tourism, with most estates offering wine-tasting facilities and many also operating restaurants or cafés. A significant feature of the Winelands is its historic towns, which include Stellenbosch, Franschhoek, Tulbagh and Paarl.*

Vergelegen Wine Estate's wine-tasting lodge

🔟 Sights

1. Stellenbosch
2. Jonkershoek Nature Reserve
3. Spier Wine Farm
4. Boschendal Wine Estate
5. Franschhoek
6. Butterfly World
7. Drakenstein Lion Park
8. Paarl
9. Tulbagh
10. Vergelegen Wine Estate

Stellenbosch

The tourist capital of the Winelands lies amidst mountainous surrounds on the banks of the Eerste River. Established just 27 years after Cape Town was settled, Stellenbosch is South Africa's second oldest town and boasts the country's highest concentration of pre-20th-century Cape Dutch buildings. Despite its overtly historic feel, Stellenbosch is anything but staid, thanks partially to the bustling student life associated with its renowned university. The compact town centre is lively – and very safe – even after dark *(see pp28–9)*.

The sandstone mountains of Jonkershoek Nature Reserve

Jonkershoek Nature Reserve

One of the Cape's most over-looked attractions, this mountainous reserve is on the outskirts of Stellenbosch. It is traversed by a selection of hiking trails, ranging from the easy paths through the reclaimed farmland of the Assegaaibosch sector, to the demanding hikes to the upper slopes. The mountain scenery hosts more than 1,000 species of *fynbos* plants and a varied selection of birds. The large mammal popu-lation – though thinly distributed – includes leopards, baboons and klipspringers. Ⓝ *Map E3*
• *Jonkershoek Valley: (021) 866 1560; open 8am–6pm daily; adm*
• *Assegaaibosch: open 8am–6pm daily; adm* • *www.capenature.co.za*

Spier Wine Farm

This estate does not aim for the gracious winelands ambience of Boschendal or Vergelegen, but adopts a more populist approach, which is why locals refer to it as "Disneyland". Excellent facilities ensure that it goes down well with children – and adults who don't take their wine too seriously. The estate has a pool, spa, playground, craft shop, cheetah outreach programme, falcon and raptors centre, horse riding and the superb four-star Spier Hotel *(see p117)*, with its impressive and striking decor. There are various restaurants and also conference facilities. Ⓝ *Map D3 • Off R310 en route Stellenbosch • (021) 809 1100 • Tasting 10am–5pm daily • www.spier.co.za*

Boschendal Wine Estate

The pioneering Boschendal Estate was first planted with vines by Huguenot settler Jean de Long in 1685. The most popular in the Stellenbosch-Franschhoek area, this estate is reached via a tree-lined drive and lies in a green valley flanked by the Groot Drakenstein and Simonsberg Mountains. The estate's Cape Dutch architecture includes a manor house dating to 1812 and a cellar built in 1795. There's a classy buffet restaurant and shady café, but on sunny days, the French-style "Le Pique Nique" on the lawns is irresistible *(see p30)*.

Franschhoek

5 Franschhoek is the self-styled culinary capital of South Africa. With a French influence that dates back to its settlement by Huguenot refugees in the late 17th century, the town's history is documented in the Huguenot Memorial and Museum lying on its outskirts. Many wine estates lie in the immediate vicinity of this small town and its upsurge as a tourist hub is reflected in the boutique shops and world-class restaurants lining the main street *(see pp30–31)*.

Butterfly World

6 Situated in Klapmuts on the R44, Butterfly World is South Africa's largest butterfly park and supports more than 20 indigenous free-flying species in an

Butterfly World

attractive, landscaped indoor garden. The fascinating Martin Filmer Spider Room, which has many different species of spiders housed in terrariums, educates visitors about the ecological value of these unjustly feared arachnids. ◎ *Map D1 • R44, Klapmuts • (021) 875 5628 • Open 9am–5pm daily • Adm*

Cape Dutch Houses

The Cape Dutch architecture that evolved in the 18th century adapted European styles to suit African conditions. Its defining feature, derived from medieval houses in Amsterdam, is an ornate round gable above the entrance. Typical buildings also have a thatched roof and an H-shaped floor plan like the manor house at Vergelegen.

Drakenstein Lion Park

7 This park was established in 1998 to provide lifelong sanctuary to captive lions that cannot be released into the wild. Housed in large enclosures, the lions can be viewed from raised platforms. Kids love it and it can be quite dramatic to visit at feeding time (4pm on Mon, Wed and Fri). ◎ *Map E1 • Old Paarl Rd, (R101), Klapmuts • (021) 863 3290 • Open 9:30am–5pm daily • Adm • www.lionrescue.org.za*

Paarl

8 Hemmed in by Paarl Mountain to the west and the Berg River to the east, the largest town in the Winelands is rather scruffy compared to Stellenbosch. However, Paarl Mountain, a fantastic granite outcrop in a pedestrian-friendly nature reserve, and the Afrikaner Taal (Language) Monument are worth a visit. The Laborie Wine estate in the town centre is charming. ◎ *Map E1 • (021) 872 0860 • www.paarlonline.com*

A rescued lion at Drakenstein Lion Park

For more details of attractions between Stellenbosch and Franschhoek, see pp30–31.

Tulbagh

The town of Tulbagh, below the Groot Winterhoek Mountains, was founded in 1700 and is relatively remote from Cape Town. It makes a charming getaway for those who want to avoid crowds. Boasting more than 30 Cape Dutch buildings, the centre exudes a period character. The *fynbos*-draped Groot Winterhoek Mountains form an imposing backdrop and offer good walking, horse riding and birdwatching opportunities. The area supports about two dozen wine estates. *Tourist information: Map U3 • (023) 230 1348 • www.tulbaghtourism.org.za*

Vergelegen Wine Estate

Translated as "lying afar", this historic property on the slopes of the Helderberg started life as a remote outpost of the Cape Colony in 1685. Fifteen years later, it became the private estate of Willem van der Stel, who established the gracious manor house and octagonal garden, and planted the gnarled camphor trees at its entrance. Visit one of South Africa's premier estates for its magnificent grounds or to sample its range of wines. *Map E4 • Lourensford Rd, Somerset West • (021) 847 1334 • Tasting 9:30am–4pm daily • Adm • www.vergelegen.co.za*

Afrikaner Taal Monument, Paarl

The "Four Passes" Day Circuit

Morning

The circuit around the **Hottentots Holland Mountains** encompasses some of the Winelands' finest scenery, architecture and wine estates. Starting in **Stellenbosch** *(see pp28–9)*, drive south along the R310 to Somerset West. Follow the signs to the **Vergelegen Wine Estate** on the Helderberg slopes. Once here, explore the historic buildings and pause for a quick snack at a local coffee shop. From Somerset West, follow the N2 east via Sir Lowry's Pass, then turn left onto the R321, passing through Grabouw and over Viljoen Pass before descending into the **Riviersonderend** (River Without End) Valley to **Theewaterskloof Dam**. Turn left onto the R45, which traverses the Franschhoek Pass, offering wonderful views over this eponymous town.

Afternoon

In **Franschhoek**, lunch at the Tasting Room at Le Quartier Francais or **Mont Rochelle's** two restaurants *(see p91)*. Then pop into the **Huguenot Memorial and Museum** or browse the shops along the main street. Continue west along the R45 and stop at **L'Ormarins Wine Estate** to visit the **Franschhoek Motor Museum** *(see p30)*. Outside Franschhoek, branch left onto the R310 to reach Stellenbosch via the **Helshoogte Pass**. Stop en route at the **Boschendal Wine Estate** *(see p83)*, the town of Pniel and Hillcrest Berry Farm. End your day with a drink at the Tokara Estate's restaurant *(see p87)*.

Left **Items at Oom Samie se Winkel** Centre **University Art Gallery** Right **Sasol Art Museum**

🔟 Galleries and Shops

University of Stellenbosch Art Gallery

Housed in a wooden-floored Lutheran church, this small gallery displays works by contemporary South African artists, including pieces by fine art students from the university.
🌐 *Map D2 • Cnr Dorp & Bird Sts • (021) 808 3524 • Open 9am–5pm Mon–Fri, 9am–1pm Sat*

Sasol Art Museum

This tiered, Neo-Classical building displays the university's collection of 19th- and 20th-century art, along with an anthropological collection of traditional African crafts and household objects. 🌐 *Map D2 • 52 Ryneveld St • (021) 808 3029 • Open 10am–4:30pm Mon 9am–4:30pm Tue–Sat*

Rupert Museum

A superb collection of contemporary South African art amassed by Dr Anton Rupert is housed in this gallery *(see p28).*

Green Sleeves

This funky little secondhand clothes shop is popular with students and a local arty crowd for its vintage clothing. Retro 70s clothes are a speciality here.
🌐 *Map D2 • 2 Crozier St, Stellenbosch • (021) 883 8374*

Oom Samie se Winkel

Stellenbosch's most famous *winkel* (shop) is over 100 years old and retains a Victorian appearance. It features an eclectic range of affordable local craftwork and genuine Africana.
🌐 *Map D2 • Dorp St • (021) 887 2372*

Karoo Classics

Handcrafted items made of mohair, ostrich leather and natural materials are the speciality at this shop in the town centre. 🌐 *Map D2 • Cnr Bird & Church Sts, Stellenbosch • (021) 886 7596 • www.karooclassics.co.za*

Touches and Tastes

With its coloured handicrafts, jewellery and candles, this annexe of Le Quartier Français *(see p116)* is a curio hunter's delight. 🌐 *Map F2 • Huguenot Rd, Franschhoek • (021) 876 2151*

Galerie Ezakwantu

The cluttered showroom of this gallery stocks high quality ethnic arts and crafts from sub-Saharan Africa. 🌐 *Map F2 • Village Centre, Huguenot Rd, Franschhoek • (021) 876 2162 • www.ezakwantu.com*

Huguenot Fine Chocolate

Delicious chocolates prepared by two local Belgian-trained chocolatiers are sold at this boutique. 🌐 *Map F2 • Huguenot Rd, Franschhoek • (021) 876 4096*

Vineyard Connection

This shop, between Stellenbosch and Paarl, stocks the Cape's finest wines and even delivers them to your home.
🌐 *Map D2 • Delvera Wine Estate • (086) 036 0360*

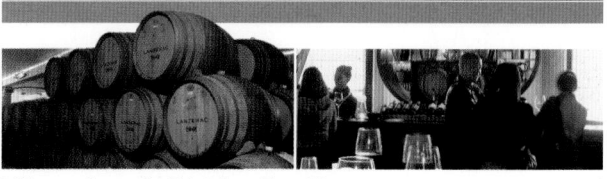

Left **Lanzerac Estate cellar** Right **Cellar at Blaauwklippen**

10 Wine Estates near Stellenbosch

Lanzerac Estate
This 17th-century estate – complete with a five-star hotel *(see p117)* – produced the world's first commercial Pinotage wine under its label in 1959.

Rustenberg Wines
This 300-year-old farm is known for its Chardonnays. ® Map E2 • Lily Rd, Idas Valley • (021) 809 1200 • Tasting 9am–4:30pm Mon–Fri, 10am–1:30pm Sat (Dec–Jan 10am–3:30pm Sat) • www.rustenberg.co.za

Tokara
Located on Helshoogte Pass, Tokara has a scenically positioned restaurant. As well as its acclaimed wines, it is known for its superb olive oil *(see p30)*.

Delaire
A "vineyard in the sky" on the crest of Helshoogte Pass, Delaire is a lovely spot for a picnic with chilled wine *(see p30)*.

Neethlingshof
The Laurentius blend and unblended wines of this estate make it a must for red-wine lovers. ® Map D3 • M12 • (021) 883 8988 • Tasting 9am–5pm Mon–Fri, 10am–4pm Sat, Sun • www.neethlingshof.co.za

Asara
Set on a hillside, Asara specializes in red wines; the Cabernet Sauvignon is recommended. ® Map D3 • M12 • (021) 888 8000 • Tasting 9am–5pm Mon–Fri, 10am–5pm Sat • www.asarawine.com

Spier Wine Farm
This family-oriented estate has mid-priced, very quaffable wines *(see p83)*.

Meerlust
At Meerlust, the cellar is stocked with the iconic claret-style Rubicon blend. ® Map D3 • R310 • (021) 843 3587 • Tasting Oct–Apr 9am–5pm Mon–Fri, 10am–4pm Sat; May–Sep 9am–4pm Mon–Fri, 10am–2pm Sat • www.meerlust.co.za

Blaauwklippen
This popular estate is home to a carriage museum and a historic manor house restaurant, and produces a quality Zinfandel. ® Map D3 • R44 • (021) 880 0133 • Tasting 9am–5pm Mon–Fri, 10am–5pm Sat, 10am–4pm Sun • www.blaauwklippen.co.za

Kanonkop
Apart from two award-winning blends, Kanonkop also produces one of the finest representatives of South Africa's Pinotage. ® Map D2 • R44 • (021) 884 4656 • Tasting 9am–5pm Mon–Fri, 9am–2pm Sat • www.kanonkop.co.za

For more detailed information on South Africa's speciality wines, see p89.

Left **Vineyards at Durbanville** Centre **Cabrière estate** Right **Wine-tasting group at La Motte**

TOP 10 Other Wine Estates

Around the Winelands

1 Durbanville Hills
Visit the Durbanville Hills estate for some excellent Merlots. ⊗ *Map C2 • M13, Tygervalley Rd (021) 558 1300 • Tasting 9am–4:30pm Mon–Fri, 9:30am–2:30pm Sat, 11am–3pm Sun • www.durbanvillehills.co.za*

2 Vergelegen
If you only visit one estate, make sure to visit Vergelegen – it is the consummate Winelands experience *(see p85)*.

3 Boschendal Wine Estate
This estate is a favourite for its scenery, architecture, wines and picnic baskets *(see p83)*.

4 La Motte
With a lovely location in the Franschhoek Valley, La Motte is growing in reputation. ⊗ *Map F2 • R45 Main Rd, Franschhoek • (021) 876 3119 • Tasting 9am–4.30pm Mon–Fri, 10am–3pm Sat • www.la-motte.com*

5 Cabrière
Cabrière is known for its world-class sparkling wines. The corks are removed with a sword. ⊗ *Map F2 • Franschhoek Pass Rd • (021) 876 8500 • Tasting 9am–5pm Mon–Fri, 10am–4pm Sat • www.cabriere.co.za*

6 Laborie
Part of the KWV collective, Laborie has a stately manor house and exudes a delightful old-world charm. ⊗ *Map E1 • Taillefert St, Paarl • (021) 807 3390 • Tasting 9am–5pm daily (Apr–Sep closed Sun) • www.laborie.co.za*

7 Rhebokskloof
Encircled by mountains, this estate is of interest mainly for its restaurant. ⊗ *Map E1 • Windmeul, Agter Paarl • (021) 869 8386 • Tasting 9am–5pm daily • www.rhebokskloof.co.za*

8 Fairview
A popular estate, Fairview produces fine wines and has a superb deli that serves hand-crafted cheese. ⊗ *Map E1 • Suid Agter Paarl Rd • (021) 863 2450 • Tasting 8:30am–5pm Mon–Fri, 8:30–4pm Sat, 9.30am–4pm Sun • www.fairview.co.za*

9 Vergenoegd
The underrated Vergenoegd has award-winning reds. ⊗ *Map C3 • Baden Powell Dr, R310 • (021) 843 3248 • Tasting 9am–5pm Mon–Fri, 9:30am–4pm Sat, 11am–4pm Sun • www.vergenoegd.co.za*

10 Zevenwacht
Apart from fine red wines, Zevenwacht's facilities include cheese-tasting and a playground. ⊗ *Map C3 • Langverwacht Rd, Kuils River • (021) 903 5123 • Tasting 8:30am–5pm Mon–Fri, 9:30am–5pm Sat, 10am–5pm Sun • www.zevenwacht.co.za*

Most estates charge a tasting fee of between R10 and R20, which typically allows you to try about 6 wines.

Left **Chenin Blanc** Centre **Boschendal Blanc de Noir and Beyerskloof Pinotage** Right **Vergelegen**

🔟 Iconic Wines to Try

1 Kanonkop Paul Sauer
The winner of numerous local and international awards, this Bordeaux-style blend is dominated by Cabernet Sauvignon, with the 2003 likely to drink well for another decade.

2 Meerlust Rubicon
Another iconic Bordeaux-style blend, this is one of South Africa's best-known wines, with several awards to its name and a reputation for benefiting from long-term cellaring.

3 Ernie Els Red Blend
The association with South Africa's top golfer may come across as a gimmick, but the wine, another Cabernet-based Bordeaux blend, is anything but, having drawn many accolades.

4 Beyerskloof Pinotage
This restaurant staple is a good introduction to Pinotage, a uniquely South African cross between Cinsaut and Pinot Noir, pioneered in 1925. It tends to produce soft, dry, medium-bodied wines with hints of banana, plum or tropical fruit.

5 Zonnebloem Shiraz (and Other Reds)
Another restaurant and supermarket staple, Zonnebloem's flavoursome reds are good for daily consumption. The Shiraz is currently the favourite, but the Pinotage and Cabernet Sauvignon are also drinkable.

6 Vergelegen White Blend
Rated "Wine of the Year" in the 2007 Platter (see below), this is an oak-matured blend of two-thirds Semillon to one-third Sauvignon Blanc. It usually improves with cellaring for two to three years.

7 Ken Forrester Chenin Blanc Range
South Africa's most heavily planted grape, comprising 18 per cent of the national vineyard, is Chenin Blanc. In the capable hands of champion winemaker Ken Forrester this grape makes great wines. His Chenin Blanc and award-winning FMC Chenin Blanc, rank with the very best.

8 Boschendal Blanc de Noir
Perfect for fans of rosé and off-dry whites, this refreshing salmon-coloured wine is made from black grapes but fermented as a white wine. It is best drunk chilled and at a summery picnic.

9 Porcupine Ridge Sauvignon Blanc
You will often come across this zesty favourite on supermarket shelves and restaurant wine lists. It is reliable and affords good value for its price.

10 JC Le Roux Scintilla
This Chardonnay-based wine is made by South Africa's leading exponent of Cap Classique, a type of sparkling wine that is almost identical to champagne.

Left **Barouche** Right **Jonkershuis at Spier Wine Farm**

TOP 10 Restaurants Around Stellenbosch

1 The Wijnhuis
With a cellar-like decor, this first-floor restaurant has one of the most extensive wine lists in Stellenbosch. It specializes in Mediterranean seafood and grills. ⊗ *Map D2 • Cnr Church & Andringa • (021) 887 5844 • RRR*

2 Volkskombuis
Set in pretty grounds along the Eerste River, Volkskombuis has been serving Cape cuisine for 30 years. On the same property, Die Oewer, with its Mediterranean menu, is a touch cheaper. ⊗ *Map D2 • Aan-de-Wagen Rd • (021) 887 2121 • RRR*

3 1802 Restaurant
This courtyard restaurant in d'Ouwe Werf has a small but imaginative menu of Malay dishes, seafood and game, and a good wine list. ⊗ *Map D2 • 30 Church St • (021) 887 4608 • RRR*

4 Bukhara Restaurant
This superb North Indian restaurant with an extensive menu is particularly strong on tandoori dishes. ⊗ *Map D2 • Cnr Dorp & Bird • (021) 882 9133 • RRRR*

5 Col'Cacchio Pizzeria
Tucked away in a mall, Stellenbosch's top pizzeria may be lacking in atmosphere, but is popular with students. A refreshing change from the heavier fare of restaurants. ⊗ *Map D2 • Simonsplein Centre • (021) 886 7088 • R*

6 Fandango Restaurant, Cocktail Bar and Internet Café
This rendezvous point hosts jazz and blues evenings in summer. The Mediterranean menu is vegetarian-friendly and is served with wine. ⊗ *Map D2 • Drostdy Centre, Bird St • (021) 887 7506 • RR*

7 Spier Wine Farm
Of the two restaurants on this estate, Jonkershuis serves Cape Malay dishes, while Moyo with its decor of Bedouin tents is more pan-African in feel. ⊗ *Map D3 • Lynedoch Rd, Stellenbosch • (021) 809 1152 • RRRR*

8 96 Winery Road
This country-style restaurant has a changing menu of seasonal dishes. It also has a private cellar of vintage Cape reds. ⊗ *Map D4 • Winery Rd (off the R44), Somerset West • (021) 842 2020 • RRR*

9 Barouche Restaurant
Set in the manor house at Blaauwklippen, Barouche serves seasonal dishes that change weekly. A kids' menu and carriage rides make it popular with families. ⊗ *Map D3 • Blaauwklippen Vineyard • (021) 880 0133 • RRR*

10 Terroir Restaurant
Set on the Kleine Zalze Estate, this restaurant's changing Provençal-style chalkboard menu combines French and local influences. ⊗ *Map D3 • Kleine Zalze Wine Estate • (021) 880 0717 • RRRR*

Credit and debit cards are accepted at all restaurants.

Price Categories

For a three course meal for one, including half a bottle of wine, cover charge, taxes and extra charges.

R	under R150
RR	R150–200
RRR	R200–250
RRRR	R250–300
RRRRR	over R300

Taki's Restaurant and Cigar Bar

Restaurants Around Franschhoek

1 The Tasting Room at Le Quartier Francais

Among the world's 50 best restaurants, patrons of the Tasting Room are served four-, six- and eight-course menus. ◈ *Map F2 • 16 Huguenot Rd • (021) 876 2151 • Closed for lunch, dinner only by reservation • RRRRR*

2 Reuben's Restaurant and Bar

Named after owner and chef Reuben Riffel, this award-winner has an innovative menu with African, Asian and European influences. ◈ *Map F2 • 19 Huguenot Rd • (021) 876 3772 • RRR*

3 Taki's Restaurant and Cigar Bar

This unapologetically smoke-filled restaurant features Greek dishes and pizzas. ◈ *Map F2 • Huguenot Rd • (021) 876 4161 • R*

4 Grande Provence Restaurant

Set on the estate of the same name, this upmarket restaurant's six-course *menu dégustation*, with a different wine accompanying each course is highly recommended. ◈ *Map F2 • Main Rd • (021) 876 8600 • RRRR*

5 Haute Cabrière Cellar Restaurant

Offering stunning views from a 17th-century estate, this restaurant serves dishes in half portions, *mezze* style. ◈ *Map F2 • Pass Rd • (021) 876 3688 • RRRRR*

6 La Petite Ferme

With a glass veranda offering views over the Franschhoek Valley, this restaurant is one of the Winelands' loveliest. The global menu does the location full justice. ◈ *Map F2 • Pass Rd • (021) 876 3016 • RRR*

7 Mange Tout Restaurant

This fine dining restaurant in the Mont Rochelle Hotel is notable for its contemporary continental cuisine. ◈ *Map F2 • Mont Rochelle, Dassenberg Rd, Franschhoek • (021) 876 2770 • RRRRR*

8 The Country Kitchen

Attached to Mont Rochelle's wine-tasting facility, this restaurant with a Mediterranean menu also puts together gourmet picnic baskets by advance order. ◈ *Map F2 • Mont Rochelle, Dassenberg Rd, Franschhoek • (021) 876 3000 • RRR*

9 Bread & Wine

With the same management as Le Quartier Français *(see p116)*, this family-oriented lunch venue on the Môreson Estate serves sumptuous meat and poultry dishes. ◈ *Map F2 • Môreson Farm • (021) 876 3692 • RR*

10 Boschendal Wine Estate

This estate has three lunch options – a buffet restaurant in the manor house, a cheerful café and French-style picnic baskets. ◈ *Map E2 • Pniel Rd, Drakenstein • (021) 870 4274 • Café: R, picnic: RR, restaurant: RRRR*

Skilpad Wildflower Reserve in Namaqualand

Beyond the Winelands

ASSUMING YOU CAN DRAG YOURSELF *away from its estimable charms,
Cape Town provides a great base for exploring the rest of the Western
Cape, a province notable for its consistently scenic coastline, fynbos-swathed
mountains and ever-expanding viniculture industry. Highlights east of Cape
Town include the peerless, land-based whale watching in Walker Bay and the
underrated De Hoop Nature Reserve – not to mention Agulhas, the most
southerly tip of Africa – while the west coast stretching up towards Lambert's
Bay combines ruggedly beautiful seaside scenery with some of the world's
most spectacular floral displays.*

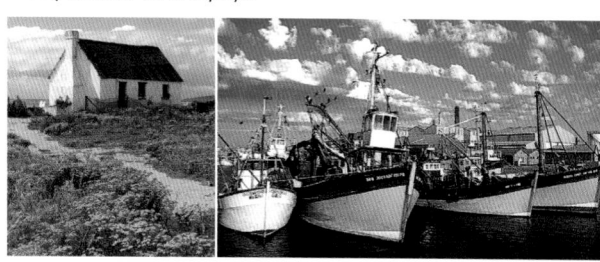

Left **A fisherman's cottage at Paternoster** Right **Fishing trawlers in Lambert's Bay harbour**

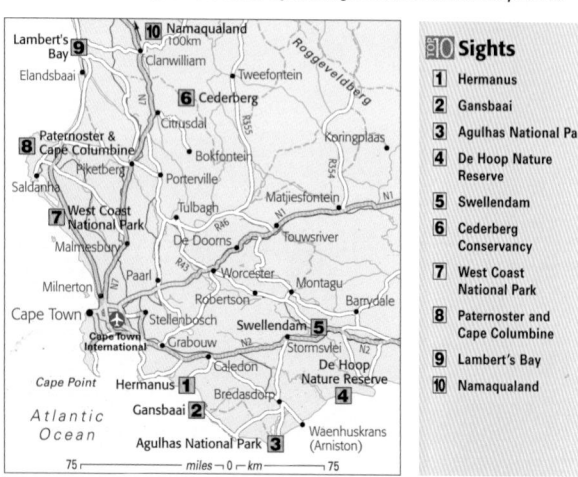

Sights

1. Hermanus
2. Gansbaai
3. Agulhas National Park
4. De Hoop Nature Reserve
5. Swellendam
6. Cederberg Conservancy
7. West Coast National Park
8. Paternoster and Cape Columbine
9. Lambert's Bay
10. Namaqualand

Preceding pages **Grapevines in Stellenbosch Vineyards**

Hermanus

Southeast of Cape Town, the quaint small town of Hermanus is perched on the sheer cliffs that hem in Walker Bay. Its attractions include the montane *fynbos* of Fernkloof Nature Reserve. But above all, Hermanus is the world's best place for some land-based whale viewing from June to November. The movements of southern right whales, which regularly breach in the waters below town, are tracked by a "whale crier". ⚅ *Map U5 • Tourist information: (028) 312 2629 • www.tourismhermanus.co.za*

Gansbaai

This fishing village, named after the geese that once nested here, is known for the sharks and whales that live offshore. Its shark safaris mostly focus on Dyer Island, which supports African penguins, black oystercatchers and the Cape fur seal colony. Nearby, the 2,000-year-old potshards unearthed at Klipgat Cave are among the oldest discovered in South Africa. ⚅ *Map U6 • Tourist information: (028) 384 1439 • www.gansbaai.com*

Eland at the De Hoop Nature Reserve

Agulhas National Park

The southernmost tip of Africa and meeting point of the Atlantic and Indian Oceans, Agulhas, named by Portuguese navigators, means "needles"— an allusion to the jagged offshore formations that have caused 250 shipwrecks. Home to South Africa's oldest lighthouse (built in 1849), its rocky beaches possess a stark charm. Proclaimed a national park in 1999, Agulhas has yet to be developed as one. ⚅ *Map V6 • (028) 435 6222 • Open 9am–5pm daily • Adm for lighthouse • www.sanparks.co.za*

De Hoop Nature Reserve

To the east of Agulhas, this is South Africa's largest surviving coastal *fynbos* habitat. It is a breeding ground for the endemic bontebok and Cape mountain zebra. The coastline of tall dunes and sheer cliffs can be explored on short walking and mountain biking trails, or along a five-day hiking trail named after the whales that breach offshore between June and November. ⚅ *Map W5 • (028) 542 1253 • Open 7am–6pm daily • Adm • www.capenature.co.za*

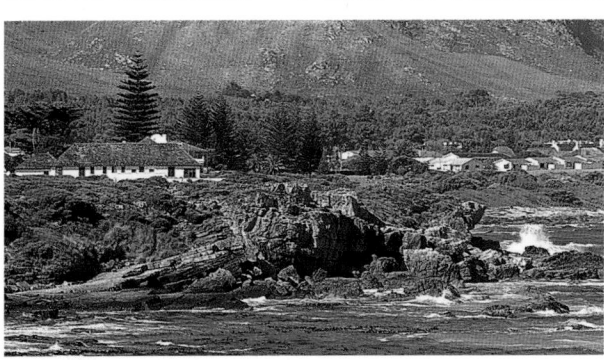

The rocky coastline around Hermanus

Whales and Dolphins

A remarkable 42 species of whales and dolphins have been recorded in South African waters. The Western Cape is the prime whale spotting destination, thanks to the southern right whales that migrate to sheltered coves such as Walkers and False Bays. Bottle-nosed dolphins are regularly seen here too, pirouetting in apparent glee as they follow a boat's wake.

Swellendam

Founded in 1745 at the Cape Colony's remote eastern frontier, this gracious small town has an old world atmosphere reinforced by Cape Dutch buildings such as the Old Drostdy (Magistrate's Seat), which was built in 1747 and is now a local history museum. Six kilometres (4 miles) out of town, a network of quiet roads and trails runs through the hilly *renosterveld* of Bontebok National Park, which was established in 1931 to protect the 30 last remaining wild bontebok, whose population has now risen to 200. ✪ *Map W5*
• *Swellendam Tourism: (028) 514 2770*
• *www.swellendamtourism.co.za*

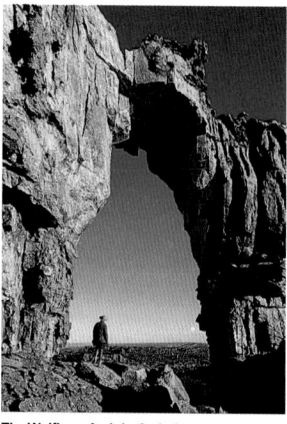

The Wolfberg Arch in Cederberg

Cederberg

The Cederberg Wilderness (Provincial Reserve) and the Cederberg Conservancy (private farmland) form the heart of Cederberg. The montane wilderness is revered in hiking circles for its stunning sandstone formations, such as the Wolfberg Arch and Maltese Cross, its profusion of prehistoric rock art and a rich endemic flora and fauna. Though best explored over several days, the conservancy also offers shorter day hikes in montane and karoo surroundings, with private camps providing access to rock art sites and views. ✪ *Map U2*
• *(027) 482 2024 • www.cederberg.co.za*

West Coast National Park

Extending around the sparkling waters of the Langebaan Lagoon, this pristine coastline lies just an hour's drive north of Cape Town. It is particularly worth visiting in August–September, when magnificent spring wildflowers bloom in the Postberg sector. Offshore islands support breeding colonies of ten different marine bird species. The recreational zone of the lagoon is popular with watersport enthusiasts. ✪ *Map S3 • (022) 772 2144/5*
• *Open Apr–Sep 7am–7:30pm; Oct–Mar 6:30am–7:30pm; Postberg: open Aug & Sep, only (flowering season) 9am–5pm*
• *Adm • www.sanparks.co.za*

Paternoster and Cape Columbine

The coastal village of Paternoster on Cape Columbine to the north of Cape Town is renowned for its traditional whitewashed fishermen's cottages and superb crayfish. The adjacent Columbine Nature Reserve protects a lovely stretch of coast that bursts into spectacular bloom from August to October and offers excellent

Renosterveld, a type of fynbos *found to the north of Cape Town, is dominated by the* renosterbos *(rhinoceros bush) shrub.*

White pelicans at Langebaan Lagoon

kayaking spots through the year. There is terrestrial and marine wildlife around too. ⓢ *Map S2*

Lambert's Bay

The largest town on the west coast, Lambert's Bay retains the feel of a sleepy port, and its pretty harbour is regularly visited by seals and other marine creatures. The main attraction is Bird Island *(see p41)* with its 20,000- to 30,000-strong colony of Cape gannets. Boat trips further afield come with a good chance of sighting the localized Heavyside's dolphin and other cetaceans. It is a good base for exploring the underrated Olifants River Wine Route.
ⓢ *Map S1 • Lambert's Bay: (027) 432 1000 • www.lambertsbay.co.za*

Namaqualand

This desert to the north of Lambert's Bay hosts one of the world's most astonishing floral spectacles. Between August and September, its parched soils, soaked by light but predictable rains, transform the rocky plains into dazzling fields of multi-hued flowers, including some 300 species of daisy and other annuals. Ten per cent of the world's succulent species are endemic to the region, including surreal tree aloes such as the *kokerbooms* (quiver trees) and bulbous *halfmensboom* (half human tree). ⓢ *Map T1 • (027) 744 1770 • www.namaqualand.com*

Overnight Tour to Hermanus

> **Day 1**

🕐 Follow the N2 east from Cape Town for 30 minutes, turning right onto the R44 at Strand. **Hermanus** *(see p95)* is 75 km (47 miles) from Strand, so you could make it in an hour, but it's worth stopping to admire the scenery. Rooiels Bay and Kleinmond offer wonderful views to **Cape Point** *(see p36)*. **Harold Porter Botanical Garden** *(see p98)* in Betty's Bay is a great place to relax in a *fynbos* habitat. In Hermanus, check into a 🏨 hotel and then lunch at the **Burgundy Restaurant** or grab a bite at beachfront **Dutchies** *(see p99)*. In the afternoon, follow the Cliff Path west out of town. Or stroll around town keeping an eye out for whales, or in calm weather, head to **Onrus Beach**. End with dinner at the **Burgundy** or 🍴 **The Marine Hermanus** *(see p118)*.

> **Day 2**

After an early breakfast, drive to **Gansbaai** *(see p95)* for a cruise to **Dyer Island** *(see p95)* to spot whales, dolphins and the fearsome great white shark. Alternatively, stay back and take a 2-hour boat-based whale cruise, or explore the town's 🛍 boutiques. If at **Gansbaai**, lunch at the trendy **Great White House** *(see p99)*. Then, if time permits, follow the longer route that connects with the N2 at Botrivier and runs west through Vredendal and Sir Lowry's Passes to **Somerset West** *(see p98)*. A detour to **Vergelegen Wine Estate** *(see p85)* in the **Helderberg Mountains** is strongly recommended.

Left **A church in the town of Robertson** Right **Harold Porter National Botanical Garden**

🔟 Best of the Rest

1 Strand
Situated 50 km (30 miles) from Cape Town, this resort town is named after the beach along its seaboard. ✪ Map D4
• www.strandtourism.com

2 Harold Porter National Botanical Garden
This garden is dedicated to *fynbos* flora. ✪ Map E6 • Betty's Bay
• (028) 272 9311 • www.sanbi.org

3 Kogelberg Biosphere Reserve
This reserve protects a *fynbos* habitat geared towards hiking, mountain biking and kayaking. ✪ Map E5 • Open 7:30am–4pm daily
• Adm • www.capenature.co.za

4 Salmonsdam Nature Reserve
At the base of the Perdeberg Mountains, this reserve is crossed by day trails through montane *fynbos*. ✪ Map V5 • Adm • www.capenature.co.za

5 Robertson
Robertson lies along the Breede River wine route, whose estates offer better value than their counterparts around Stellenbosch and Franschhoek. ✪ Map V4 • www.robertsonr62.com

6 Ceres
Named after the Roman goddess of agriculture, Ceres lies in the main centre of deciduous fruit production. ✪ Map U3
• www.ceres.org.za

7 Karoo National Botanical Garden
An uncultivated garden protecting over 400 species including the impressive *kokerboom*. ✪ Map U4 • Roux Rd • Open 7am–7pm daily
• Free except Aug–Oct • www.sanbi.org

8 Melkbosstrand
A holiday spot north of Cape Town, popular with anglers, with a fine beach that offers views across Table Bay. ✪ Map T4

9 Darling
This once quaint town's Victorian railway station is now the venue for the risqué cabaret, Evita se Perron *(see p67)*.
✪ Map T3 • www.darlingtourism.co.za

10 Rocher Pan Nature Reserve
The bird species known from this seasonal wetland include the great white pelican and the great crested grebe. ✪ Map S2
• Open May–Aug 8am–5pm daily; Sep–Apr 7am–6pm daily • Adm • www.capenature.co.za

For more information about fynbos *flora,* **see pp76–9.**

Price Categories

For a three-course meal for one, including half a bottle of wine, cover charge, taxes and extra charges.

R	under R150
RR	R150–200
RRR	R200–250
RRRR	R250–300
RRRRR	over R300

Agulhas Country Lodge

TOP 10 Lunch Stops

1 Seafood
This restaurant, in the five-star Marine Hermanus, is an excellent bet for a seafood lunch best enjoyed with the great wine list and a view of the legendary whales in the Walker Bay waters.
◉ Map U5 • Marine Dr, Hermanus • (028) 313 1000 • RRRRR

2 Dutchies
The cosmopolitan food at Dutchies is enhanced by the attractive beachfront location. A great spot for watching whales.
◉ Map U5 • Grotto Beach, Hermanus • (028) 314 1392 • R

3 Burgundy Restaurant
This sea-view restaurant has a sophisticated menu with influences from the north and south of the Mediterranean. It is in one of the oldest buildings in Hermanus, which is now a heritage site. ◉ Map U5 • Marine Dr, Hermanus • (028) 312 2800 • RR

4 The Great White House
A gathering place for those about to embark on whale-and shark-watching trips. Specializing in fabulous seafood, early breakfasts are also provided as well as light meals seven days a week. ◉ Map U6 • 5 Geelbek St, Kleinbaai, Gansbaai • (028) 384 3273 • RR

5 Agulhas Country Lodge
This hillside lodge is the pick of a somewhat limited choice of eateries in Agulhas. Excellent seafood and wine along with

sublime views over Africa's most southerly point are the main draws. ◉ Map U6 • Cape Agulhas • (028) 435 7650 • RRRR

6 Togryers Restaurant
Now a national monument, the former toll house at Mitchell's Pass is known for its steaks. It also offers country fare and light lunches. ◉ Map U3 • Ceres • (023) 312 1211 • R

7 Geelbek Restaurant
Located in a Cape Dutch house, Geelbek Restaurant specializes in South African fare, and has a reasonable vegetarian selection. ◉ Map S3 • West Coast National Park • (022) 772 2134 • RRR

8 Slipway Waterfront Restaurant
This waterfront restaurant is known for locally cultivated mussels and oysters and features affordable west coast wines. ◉ Map S3 • Saldanha Bay • (022) 714 4235 • RR

9 Strandloper Restaurant
This eatery offers a tasty barbecue buffet of local crayfish. ◉ Map S3 • Langebon Lagoon • (022) 772 2490 • Open for lunch on weekends and some weekdays • RR

10 Muisbosskerm Restaurant
Linger over the buffet of Cape dishes at this restaurant on the beachfront. ◉ Map S1 • 5 km south of Lamberts Bay • (027) 432 1017 • www.muisbosskerm.co.za • RR

Following pages **Miniature ethnic masks, Greenmarket Square**

STREETSMART

CAPE TOWN & THE WINELANDS' TOP 10

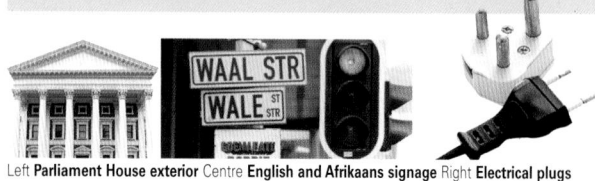

Left **Parliament House exterior** Centre **English and Afrikaans signage** Right **Electrical plugs**

🔟 General Information

1 Government

South Africa has been a multi-party democracy with an independent judiciary since May 1994. The Parliament, situated in Cape Town, comprises a representative National Assembly and National Council of Provinces. The dominant party since 1994 has been the African National Congress (ANC). The official opposition is the Democratic Alliance. Jacob Zuma, leader of the ANC, became president in May 2009.

2 Economy

South Africa has Africa's strongest economy and accounts for half the continent's mineral and industrial output. Cape Town is one of four main economic hotspots and the national leader in the tourist sector. Its average growth of 3–4 per cent since 1999 has been somewhat tempered in recent times.

3 Languages

South Africa has 11 official languages: Afrikaans, English, isiNdebele, isiXhosa, isiZulu, Sepedi, Sesotho, Setswana, siSwati, Tshivenda and Xitsonga. The most widely spoken language in the Cape Town area is Afrikaans, followed by isiXhosa and English. English however, is sufficient for almost all practical purposes.

4 Religions

Though there is freedom of worship, Christianity is dominant, with Zionist, Catholic, Methodist, Dutch Reformed and Anglican being the most common. The remaining population follows Islam, Judaism, other religions or are atheists.

5 Electricity

Very rare, localized cuts are experienced in Cape Town. All hotel rooms take the British Standard earthed plug. Most have adaptors for the twin-pronged unearthed plugs used in continental Europe.

6 Opening Hours

Post offices and government offices are open 8:30am–4:30pm Monday to Friday. Post offices are also open on Saturdays 8:30–11:30am. Timings for sights like museums and wine estates vary greatly *(see also p108 and p111)*.

7 Time Zone

South Africa is one or two hours ahead of the UK, six hours ahead of Eastern Standard Time and eight hours behind Australian Standard Time.

8 Embassies

Diplomatic representation is in Pretoria (Tshwane) in Gauteng Province. The UK, the USA and Germany have consulates in Cape Town.

9 Public Holidays

South Africa has 12 annual holidays from the global to the national: 1 Jan (New Year's Day), 21 March (Human Rights Day), Good Friday, Easter Monday, 22 April (Freedom Day), 1 May (Workers' Day), 16 June (Youth Day), 9 Aug (National Women's Day), 24 Sep (Heritage Day), 16 Dec (Day of Reconciliation), 25 Dec (Christmas) and 26 Dec (Day of Goodwill).

10 Further Reading

Tremendous literature by prominent novelists include works by Andre Blink, Achmat Dangor and Nobel prize winners JM Coetzee and Nadine Gordimer. Anthony Sampson's *Mandela: The Authorised Biography* and Mandela's autobiography, *Long Walk to Freedom*, are popular non-fiction books. A range of field guides focusing on the country's mammals, reptiles, trees and flowers can be picked up in any bookshop in Cape Town.

Consulates

UK Consulate
• (021) 405 2400

US Consulate
• (021) 702 7300

German Consulate
• (021) 464 3000

Visitors are often confused by the fact that any public holiday due to fall on a Sunday is carried over to the following Monday.

Left **An Internet café** Centre **Tourist information sign** Right **Customs banner at the airport**

TOP10 Planning Your Trip

1 Tourist Information

Cape Town Tourism is the official Visitor Services Organization, with 20 world-class information centres within the city. Visit them for information about reservation and other auxiliary services.
Ⓢ (021) 487 6800.• www.tourismcapetown.co.za

2 Internet Resources

Many websites are dedicated to travel in Cape Town the most useful being the official tourist board (www.tourismcapetown.co.za). The unofficial www.capetown.org and the listings-oriented www.capetowntoday.co.za are also popular. For Winelands coverage, www.wineroutes-sa.co.za is useful, while foodies are pointed to www.eatout.co.za and www.restaurants.co.za.

3 Maps

Tourist offices in Cape Town stock a good selection of free maps and you can pick up plans for smaller towns at tourist offices. For detailed maps, Map Studio has the best. Ⓢ Map Studio: Freeway Park on Upper Camp • (021) 510 4311 • www.mapstudio.co.za

4 Passports and Visas

Your passport should not be due to expire within six months of your intended date of departure from South Africa. It must contain at least two unused pages for stamps. Visas are not required by nationals of EU countries, the USA, Canada, Australia and New Zealand, who are granted a free three-month temporary visitor's permit upon arrival. Citizens of most other countries require a visa.

5 Customs

No customs duty is charged on items imported temporarily for personal use. Otherwise duty-free restrictions are standard.

6 Insurance

Travel insurance is highly recommended; there is no public health service, which means that all medical bills of uninsured travellers will have to be paid from their own pockets.

7 When to Go

The summer months of October–March are the peak tourist season, when facilities tend to be pricier. Winter is more of a lottery, with periods of beautiful, mild weather interspersed by days of cold, drizzle and wind. Late August–September is perfect; not too crowded, balanced weather and wonderful spring wildflowers on display.

8 What to Wear

Weather tends to be warm to mild in summer, so choose your wardrobe accordingly, and add in a couple of sweaters just in case. The winters (May–September) are cold and wet, making a jacket essential. Skimpily clad women may be subject to unwanted male attention, unless at a beach.

9 What to Pack

Arm yourself against the sun with sunblock and a hat, especially if you are coming from the northern winter. Carry binoculars to spot wildlife. Stock up on prescription drugs but there's no need to be over-prepared – anything you forget can be bought in Cape Town.

10 How Long to Stay

Anything less than a week for Cape Town and the Winelands would feel restrictively short. It is easily possible to spend two weeks holidaying in and around the city and stay busy.

Tourist Information Offices

The Pinnacle Building
Map Q4 • Cnr Burg and Castle Sts • (021) 487 6800

Stellenbosch
Map D2 • 36 Market St • (021) 883 3584

The V&A Waterfront
Map Q2 • Clock Tower • (021) 405 4500

Left **Cape Town International Airport** Right **A taxi in Cape Town**

🔟 Getting to Cape Town

1 Flights from the USA and Europe

The main gateway for international flights to South Africa is OR Tambo International Airport in Johannesburg. It is connected to Cape Town by numerous domestic flights. A number of operators also fly directly to Cape Town from North America or Europe, notably British Airways and South African Airways (SAA) (www. flysaa.com).

2 Flights from within Africa

SAA operates a network of direct flights to African capital cities. Most major African national carriers fly between their capital city and South Africa, with connections to Europe and North America. Flights from elsewhere in Africa, land in Johannesburg from where Cape Town-bound travellers need to catch a domestic flight.

3 Domestic Flights

The arrival of smaller airlines has ensured that cheap flights are available between Cape Town and other cities. You can shop online for details on such carriers as Mango, Kulula, Nationwide and 1time *(see p107)*.

4 Airports

The Cape Town International Airport flanks the N2 highway 20 km (13 miles) east of the city centre. It is one of the busiest airports in Africa and has an extensive range of shops and restaurants. ✆ *(021) 937 1200 • www.airports. co.za*

5 Airport Hotels

With the isolated location of Cape Town International Airport on the Cape Flats, travellers arriving late or leaving early may elect to stay in the inexpensive but well-equipped 90-room Road Lodge, the only hotel adjacent to the airport. ✆ *Map C3 • (021) 934 7303 • www.citylodge.co.za*

6 Leaving the Airport

Some hotels offer free airport transfers. Otherwise, Randy's operates a regular shuttle to and from the city centre, the V&A Waterfront, Green Point and Camps Bay at R200 for a ride into town, depending on destination and group size. Private taxis are available at a higher price, as are several rental cars. ✆ *Randy's: (021) 706 0166 • www.randystours.com*

7 Intercity Buses

Intercity buses connect Cape Town to Johannesburg, Pretoria, Port Elizabeth, Durban and Upington. The fares are inexpensive. Major operators include Greyhound (www.grey hound.co.za), Intercape (www.intercape.co.za),

Translux (www.translux. co.za), and Intercity Xpress (www.intercity. co.za).

8 Self-Drive

Car rental rates start at R150 per day and include 200 km (125 miles) free usage. Most major international players are represented. International operators such as Avis (www.avis. co.za) and Hertz (www. hertz.co.za) are costlier than local companies such as AA Car Hire (www.aacarhire capetown.co.za) and Tempest Sixt (www. tempestcarhire.co.za).

9 Trains

Few tourists use passenger trains as they are not safe, but details are available at www.spoor net.co.za. Popular exceptions are the Blue Train between Pretoria or Johannesburg and Cape Town (www.bluetrain.co. za) and the luxurious trains of Rovos Rail (www.rovosrail.co.za).

10 Ocean Cruises

An unusual way to get to Cape Town is by one of the cruise ships that dock there en route to Indian Ocean Islands and Europe. Particularly legendary is the world's last operating mail ship, the *RMS St Helena* (www.rms-st-helena. com) running annually between Southampton and St Helena.

Left **Filling station** Centre **Car rental agency** Right **Local bus on city roads**

Getting Around

1 Rikki Taxis
Fulfilling a function somewhere between normal cabs and African "shared taxis", these cabs can be booked by phone or hailed on the street through the city centre and select suburbs. There are "Rikki Phone" at various locations. They take up to six people and are far cheaper than bona fide taxis. ⓢ *(086) 174 5547*
• *Hours: 6:30am–midnight Mon–Fri, 24 hours Sun*
• *www.rikkis.co.za*

2 Taxis
Taxis in the city are inexpensive by international standards at around R10/km. There are few roving taxis, but you can hire one at a taxi rank (Long St, outside most major upmarket hotels and malls) or ring an operator. ⓢ *Marine: (021) 434 0434; Sea Point Taxis: (021) 434 4444; Unicab: (021) 448 1720*

3 Car Rental
The Cape Peninsula and the Winelands are well suited to self-driving. The distances are quite small, so you should be alright within the free limit of 150–200 km (94–125 miles) that is imposed by most companies. Do be aware that the additional "per km" costs will build up quickly if you do something like drive between Johannesburg and Cape Town!

4 Filling Stations
Most filling stations stay open 24 hours and have decent shops attached. The price of fuel falls somewhere between fuel costs in Europe and the USA, and can be paid for with a credit or debit card. Some stations only accept a locally issued petrol card, so you'll need to pay cash.

5 Parking
Multi-storey car parks dot the city. Car parks are also attached to tourist attractions such as the Company's Garden and Castle of Good Hope. Most streets have an attendant who'll guard your car for a tip (R2–5).

6 Bicycles
Probably inadvisable in the city centre, cycling can be a very enjoyable way of getting around the sunny countryside, provided you're aware of the considerable distances between places. A recommended agency for bike rental is Downhill Adventures (021 422 0388), www.downhill adventures.com).

7 Walking
This is the cheapest – and healthiest – way of getting about and most major attractions in central Cape Town are within walking distance of each other. It is advisable to avoid wearing valuables. Take advice

from locals about where to go after dark; avoid walking alone. If in doubt hail a taxi cab or a Rikki.

8 Buses
The hub for metropolitan bus services is the Golden Acre Bus Terminal on Strand Street. The bus network is more limited in out-lying suburbs. The open-top sightseeing buses are popular with tourists *(see p107)*.

9 Trains
The main railway station is on Adderley Street. A great experience is the "hop-on, hop-off" ticket available on the scenic southern line between Cape Town and Simon's Town. On purchasing the ticket, you will get a map detailing sights within easy reach of key stations along the route. There's a regular service to Stellenbosch. ⓢ *(080) 065 6463 • Ticket: 1st class R23–50, 2nd class R14–50*
• *www.capemetrorail.co.za*

10 Organized Excursions
Without private transport, organized excursions are the best way to get to remote places such as the Cape of Good Hope Nature Reserve *(see p26)*. They are also the safest option to visit townships or to explore the Winelands. Hotels or tourist offices can recommend operators.

If you do plan to cycle around the Cape Peninsula, be aware that it is forbidden to carry bicycles on metropolitan trains.

Left **Ostrich on the road** Centre **A tube of sunscreen** Right **Cloud cover over Table Mountain**

TOP 10 Things to Avoid

1 Road Hazards

South Africans are known for their assertive driving style, and Capetonians are no exception. Be particularly cautious of the notoriously whimsical minibuses that serve as public transport. In the rural Winelands, be alert to the possibility of livestock suddenly crossing the road and drunken pedestrians weaving in front of your vehicle.

2 Sun

People who are unused to the ozone-depleted, cloudless southern sky are inclined to underestimate the strength of the sun here (see p109). Wear strong sunblock and a wide-brimmed hat whilst out walking, as well as on boat trips, when the reflection from the water intensifies the sun's rays.

3 Snakes

Although snakes are present on Table Mountain and in nature reserves, most species are harmless; even the venomous ones tend to flee when they sense the seismic vibration of an approaching human foot. The risk of snakebite can be further reduced by wearing solid shoes and trousers on nature trails. Also be sure that you avoid rummaging through woodpiles or picking up stones with gloveless hands.

4 Feeding Baboons

Baboons fed by people perceive them as a source of food, which can lead to aggressive confrontations. Deliberately feeding a baboon encourages this, and may eventually lead to it being shot. All the same, should one confront you over food, surrender the titbit immediately – the doglike incisors of a baboon can inflict a nasty bite.

5 HIV and AIDS

The rate of HIV infection in South Africa is very high. The most certain way to avoid infection is abstinence. Failing that, condoms can provide a high level of protection; these can be bought at pharmacies, supermarkets and convenience stores at filling stations.

6 ATM Scams

Two scams are associated with ATMs. One involves a helpful local making off with your card, while the other entails causing cards to get stuck mid-transaction. You are most vulnerable outside of banking hours and at remote locations. Never reveal your PIN to a stranger and ensure nobody can see it when you type it in.

7 Mugging

The odds of being mugged are small, provided that you follow common sense advice and exercise caution (see p109). In the unlikely event you are accosted, you're likely to walk away unscathed if you cooperate with your assailants.

8 Weather Changes on the Mountain

The fickle weather of Table Mountain claims a few lives every year. Don't even think about hiking on the mountain in stormy weather. Even on clear days, be alert to the possibility of changing conditions. Should mist suddenly descend, do the same – though if visibility is poor, it is best to wait for help.

9 Swimming in Dangerous Conditions

Although the occasional shark attack tends to grab headlines, a bigger danger to swimmers is riptides and other strong currents in stormy weather. Never swim without seeking local advice, in poor weather or where no other swimmers are present.

10 Drunk-Driving on Wine Routes

Driving after wine-tasting is potentially dangerous, and is illegal. Unless you have a designated driver who's prepared to abstain, join one of the inexpensive day tours operating out of Cape Town or Stellenbosch (see pp28–9).

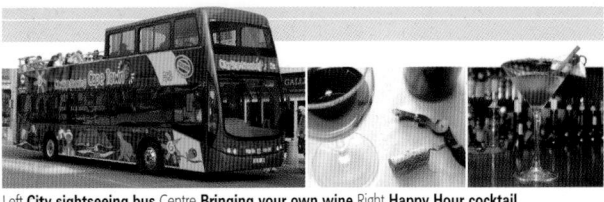

Left **City sightseeing bus** Centre **Bringing your own wine** Right **Happy Hour cocktail**

🔟 Budget Tips

1 Cheap Domestic Flights
A boom in domestic carriers has led to wide availability of cheap air tickets – indeed, if you are flexible about dates, it may well be cheaper to fly between Johannesburg or Durban and Cape Town than to take a coach or train. For more information, try www.flymango.com, www.kulula.com, www.flynationwide.co.za, www.flysaa.com and www.1time.aero

2 Off-Season Hotel Rates
As with any seasonal destination, Cape Town has a glut of empty rooms during the low season. Several hotels offer fantastic walk-in and last-minute online rates from May to September, sometimes as low as R300 for a double room (little more than a backpacker hostel). Check Protea and City Lodge chains for good deals. See www.citylodge.co.za and www.proteahotels.co.za for information.

3 Free Activities
Although entrance fees to Cape Town's main tourist attractions are generally reasonable, they quickly add up. You can save a packet by using free alternatives. Set a day aside to walk up Table Mountain rather than using the cableway or walk up Lion's Head, spend an afternoon feeding pigeons and watching squirrels in the Company's Garden or take a long stroll along Noordhoek Beach.

4 Happy Hour
Many bars in Cape Town have a Happy Hour, when drinks are half-price, or you get a second drink for the price of one. Ask around!

5 Mini-bus Taxis
Mini-buses generally operate along Victoria, Regent and Strand roads, and Long, Kloof and Buitenkant streets from early morning to evening. Shared taxis can be flagged down as one passes or while standing at a bus stop. Always ask where their final stop is before embarking. Tell the driver when you want to get off and thank him or her, when alighting. Fares range from R3.50 to R4.50.

6 City Sightseeing Buses
A popular, inexpensive way of getting around Cape Town is the open-topped hop-on, hop-off City Sightseeing Bus, which follows two routes – the Green Route and the Blue Route. It costs R100 for a day's unlimited usage. ◎ (021) 511 6000 • www.citysightseeing.co.za

7 Cheap Day Tours
Cheap day tours are more convenient than public transport and are cheaper than taxis. Tours offered by several companies include outings to Cape Point and Boulders, wine-tasting tours, township visits and adventure activities. You can book tours through the agencies along Long Street.

8 Bring Your Own Wine (Corkage)
Many restaurants allow diners to bring their own wine, which often saves on the price charged on the wine list, even where a corkage fee (typically R20–30) is levied. Check ahead when you call in for a reservation.

9 Picnic and Self-Catering
Cape Town is studded with good supermarkets, and canny travellers can save a small fortune in restaurant bills by self-catering, or putting together picnic baskets. Excellent picnic spots include the Company's Garden, Boulders Beach, or wine estates around Stellenbosch.

10 Use Your Feet
The cheapest way to get around is, of course, on foot. The compact districts of Cape Town, Stellenbosch and Franschhoek all reward pedestrian exploration. Keen walkers could extend their rambling to include suburban wine estates such as Mont Rochelle or Lanzerac.

The hop-on, hop-off Baz Bus (www.bazbus.co.za) connects Johannesburg to Cape Town via Durban and the Garden Route.

Left **ATM** Centre **Post and courier service** Right **Local newspapers**

🔟 Banking and Communications

1 Currency
South Africa's currency is the rand, divided into 100 cents, locally denoted by the symbol R, and internationally by the prefix ZAR. Bank notes are in denominations of R10, R20, R50, R100 and R200. Coins come in denominations of R5, R2, R1, 50c, 20c, 10c and 5c.

2 Banking Hours
Most banks are open 9am–3:30pm Monday–Friday. City banks are open 8:30–11:30am on Saturday, but this may not be the case in small towns. Banks at international airports generally stay open late into the night.

3 Foreign Exchange
Most banks have foreign exchange facilities, and private bureaux de changes (locally called forex bureaux) are also found in malls and airports, typically keeping longer hours than banks. Most hotels also offer exchange facilities but at comparatively poor rates. All foreign exchange transactions are documented and you are required to show your passport. Exchange rates are non-negotiable and there is no black market.

4 Credit Cards
Major international credit and debit cards are accepted by practically all hotels, restaurants, shops and other outlets dealing with tourists. The most widely accepted card is Visa, followed by MasterCard. American Express is less widely used in South Africa, and may not always be accepted. You will be asked for "cheque" or "savings", which can be ignored. Market stalls and small enterprises expect cash.

5 ATMs
Most banks have at least one ATM where cash can be withdrawn using international cards, typically to a value of R1,000 (around US$113) per transaction. There are also ATMs in many airports and filling station shops. ATM-associated crime is common, so be careful when you withdraw money (see p106).

6 Telephone
Local and international calls can be made from most phone booths and hotel rooms. Cape Town has a 021 prefix and the international code for South Africa is +27. Calls out of South Africa are prefixed by 00. Mobile (cell) phones are in wide use and numbers start with 07 or 08.

7 Internet
Internet cafés with broadband are dotted all over Cape Town and are generally quite cheap.

Most hotels also offer Internet facilities, but at inflated rates. Wi–Fi is available at international airports, cafés, restaurants and select hotels. If you need it, it is best to check if the hotel has the facility before you make a reservation.

8 Post, Shipping and Courier
International post in and out of South Africa is reliable but slow – airmail to Europe typically takes about a week and to North America at least two weeks. A faster service is offered by a private chain called PostNet, found in most large malls. Use an international courier such as FedEx or DHL for items of value.

9 Newspapers
Unlike during apartheid, South Africa now has freedom of press. Several English-language newspapers are available in Cape Town, notably the *Cape Argus, Sunday Times* and the *Weekly Mail & Guardian*.

10 Television
Public TV is restricted to three channels operated by state broadcaster SABC and privately run eTv. Both are heavy on American fare and loud advertising. Most hotels and sports bars have cable TV offering an array of movie, sports and international news.

 Expect to use your mobile a lot in South Africa. You can save money by buying a local SIM card or renting a phone at airport kiosks.

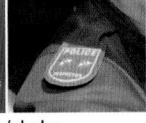

Left **A Cape Town pharmacy** Centre **Private medical service** Right **Policeman's badge**

🔟 Security and Health

1 Medical Insurance

Medical insurance is practically essential, as you'll be dependent on private healthcare facilities in the case of illness. Standards of private healthcare are high, and it is relatively cheap compared to the USA or Europe.

2 Vaccinations

Vaccinations advised for trips to most tropical countries aren't really applicable to the Cape Town area, though you should get polio or tetanus boosters if these have expired. No vaccination is mandatory for North Americans or Europeans, but anybody coming via a yellow fever area (anywhere else in Africa) might be asked to show a vaccination certificate at immigration.

3 Emergency Numbers

Nationwide emergency numbers are 10111 for the police and 10177 for ambulance (no area code required). Local emergency numbers will be listed in your hotel directory, though it is best to inquire at the reception before dialling.

4 Medical Facilities and Pharmacies

The Cape Town area is serviced by several hospitals that broadly conform to Western standards. Other facilities such as dentists and physiotherapists are also widely available – ask your hotel for a local recommendation. Pharmacies are scattered over the city, but the only 24-hour one is M-Kem on Durban Road next to the N1 highway (021 948 5706).

5 Malaria

Although malaria is present in South Africa, it is restricted to the northern and eastern border areas. There is no need to take precautions if your travels are restricted to the Western Cape, which is entirely malaria-free, but seek advice about prophylactic drugs if you plan on visiting Kruger Park or the coastal belt north of Durban.

6 Sunburn

Excessive exposure to the harsh sun is a perennial hazard for tourists hailing from gloomier climes. Overdo the sunbathing and you risk a painful sunburn or, in extreme cases, severe sunstroke. Dedicated sun-worshippers are advised to smother themselves in strong sunblock and to restrict tanning to one hour, preferably when the sun is low in the sky.

7 Drinking Water

You can assume that all tap water in Cape Town is safe to drink unless you have been specifically warned to the contrary. Bottled water is widely available for those who prefer it.

8 Public Toilets

Public toilets are generally maintained to Western standards, though facilities are occasionally on the grubby side. Most filling stations and shopping malls have well sign-posted toilets. In the city centre you may need to look a little harder – or ask nicely and slip into a restaurant or hotel.

9 Mugging and Crime

Avoid carrying large sums of cash, and having any cameras loose. Do not leave your belongings unattended. In general take advice from locals about where to go after dark *(see p106)*. In particular, take precautions at lonely lookout points, especially after dusk.

10 Dangerous Wildlife

Snakes and scorpions present a small but real danger when walking in nature reserves, so counter the threat by wearing solid shoes and long trousers. Shark attacks occur sporadically in False Bay, often on surfers. However, the risk is slight compared to, say, a car accident, and can be reduced by avoiding swimming with an open wound or between dusk and dawn, when sharks are most active.

Although people associate Africa with fierce wildlife, Cape Town's only potentially dangerous mammals are baboons (see p106).

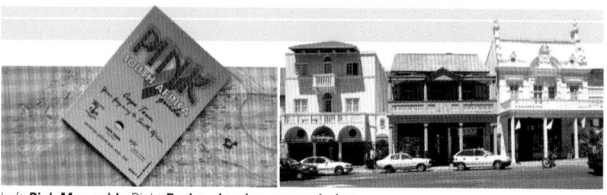

Left *Pink Map* guide Right **Backpackers' accommodation**

TOP 10 Special Concerns

1 Disabled Travellers
Though facilities for disabled travellers in South Africa are not very sophisticated, the situation is improving. Most hotels, malls and tourist sights have wheelchair access. The main paths at Kirstenbosch are wheelchair-friendly and also have a Braille Trail. Check www.eco-access.org.za for details of wheelchair accessibility at various other reserves countrywide. If you plan on renting a car, be sure to ask for a special parking disk that allows for parking concessions.

2 Special Needs Tour Operators
Several tour operators specialize in itineraries for disabled travellers. Flamingo Tours (www.flamingotours.co.za) and Endeavour Safaris (www.endeavour-safaris.com) are both experienced and offer itineraries catering to most disabilities. A recommended operator on a national level is Rolling South Africa (www.rollingsa.co.za).

3 Women Travellers
Attitudes towards women are less enlightened than in most Western nations, but many women travel alone in South Africa. However, dress conservatively in rural areas and be sure to avoid walking alone in lonely areas or after dark.

4 Backpackers
Cape Town is a backpackers' hotspot with several dozen hostels catering to budget travellers. It also offers an excellent selection of short and long tours, locally and further afield. The website www.coastingafrica.com is an invaluable resource for backpackers, as is the associated free booklet, *Coast To Coast*.

5 Camping
There are plenty of good campsites around Cape Town and in most nature reserves, usually with good washing facilities and cooking areas. It is a great way to experience this beautiful region, especially if you have wheels, but lugging around a tent and gear can be quite restrictive.

6 Students
Travellers under the age of 26 or registered students may obtain reduced rates at certain tourist attractions and on public transport upon production of a valid student card.

7 Travel with Children
Cape Town has plenty to offer kids of all ages. Most hotels give significant discounts to youngsters (or allow them to share their parents' room for free) and many restaurants have inexpensive menus for children. Entrance fees to the sights and attractions for kids are typically half to one-quarter of the adult fee.

8 Senior Travellers
Cape Town is a popular destination with senior travellers; facilities for seniors are better here than elsewhere in Africa. Substantial discounts on many services and activities are offered.

9 Gay and Lesbian Travellers
South Africa has an enlightened constitution when it comes to gay and lesbian rights. Cape Town is the main hub of the country's homosexual community and is recognized as a leading gay destination. Elsewhere in South Africa, however, on-the-ground attitudes tend to lag behind official policy; overt homosexual behaviour could attract unwanted trouble.

10 Gay Resources
The gay travel sites, www.capetown.tv and www.capeinfoafrica.co.za include information about gay-friendly guesthouses and facilities. A more hard-hitting source of gay news and views, www.capetownpride.co.za is also the official site of the Cape Town Pride Festival, taking place over February–March (*see p54*). The *Pink Map* is another good source of information.

110

For details on disabled facilities available, contact the Association for Persons with Physical Disabilities at (021) 555 2881.

Streetsmart

Left **The V&A Waterfront shopping centre** Centre **Self-catering accommodation** Right **Tipping**

Shopping, Eating and Hotel Tips

Shopping Hours

Shopping hours are usually 9am–5pm Monday–Friday, but some outlets stay open until 6pm. Stores in malls such as Victoria Wharf (The V&A Waterfront) stay open until 9pm. Shops that are open on weekends have shorter trading hours.

VAT Refunds

Non-resident foreign passport holders on a visit to South Africa can claim a VAT refund of 14 per cent on all purchases over R250 intended for export. This is best done before leaving; it involves presenting all invoices to VAT refund offices at Cape Town International Airport or the OR Tambo International Airport in Johannesburg. ✪ *Vat Refund: Clock Tower Bldg, The V&A Waterfront • Open 9am–5pm Mon–Sat, 10am–5pm Sun.*

Crafts and Curios

Cape Town is a great place to buy crafts from around Africa, with markets and shops at the V&A Waterfront, on Long Street, along the central railway station, at Hout Bay's fishing harbour and on the main road through Kalk Bay.

Breakfasts

Most smart hotels include breakfast in the room rate. Typically, this will be an extensive buffet of hot and cold dishes that sets you up for the day. Where it isn't included in the room rate, you'll be better off grabbing a hot drink and croissant at one of the delicatessens and coffee shops scattered around. Kloof Street is a good place for cheap breakfasts.

Lunches

When out sight-seeing, you can grab a bite to eat at any of the eateries that are attached to most of the tourist attractions. On more leisurely summer days, a lingering seafood lunch at the Waterfront is highly recommended, ideally accompanied by a bottle of crisp white wine.

Dinners

For most locals, dinner is the main meal of the day. If you eat out, it is usually a three-course affair served with red wine. Money conscious tourists should note that starters and desserts tend to push up the price of a meal, and a well-chosen main course should suffice. In summer, it is pleasant to eat dinner alfresco, but this isn't realistic over May–September.

Picnicking

A popular lunchtime option on the Wine Route is to picnic on the lawn of your chosen estate – Boschendal and Spier in particular provide excellent picnic baskets, as does the Silvertree Deli in Kirstenbosch. You can also put together a picnic lunch at a supermarket.

Tipping

Waiters and bar staff tend to be paid very poorly and depend on tips, which should be in the 10–15 per cent range depending on the quality of service. Give cash rather than adding the tip to your bill and paying by card. It is customary to tip hotel porters around R2–5 per bag. Elsewhere, tips are discretionary.

Self-Catering Accommodation

Opting for self-catering accommodation can save you from running up high restaurant bills and also offers greater freedom of choice. For self-catering properties in and around Cape Town, try Cape Letting (www.capeletting.com). Most backpacker hostels offer communal self-catering facilities.

Seasonal Discounts

The low season (May–September) is a good time for last-minute deals. Check websites of chains such as Protea and City Lodge and you may find three-star hotel rooms going for as little as R300–400. If you can't find a good deal online, book into a hotel for your first night and look for cheaper walk-in options once you are there.

Left **12 Apostles Hotel & Spa** Right **The Grand Daddy**

Upmarket Hotels

1 Mount Nelson Hotel

With marshmallow-pink Victorian exteriors, elegant rooms, a fine restaurant and grand views, the "Nellie" is the city's most prestigious hotel. The high teas served with obsequious gravity on the patio are reminiscent of a bygone era. ⊗ *Map P6 • 76 Orange St • (021) 483 1000 • www. mountnelson.co.za • RRRRR*

2 One&Only Cape Town

An urban resort with contemporary African flair in the heart of fashionable Victoria & Alfred Waterfront. It has 131 rooms and suites, 40 of them on an island. ⊗ *Map P2 • Dock Rd, V&A Waterfront • (082) 840 3633 • www.oneandonlyresorts • RRRRR*

3 Derwent House

This boutique hotel, located in the heart of the City Bowl, has rooms with views of Table Mountain. The stylish decor is complemented by excellent facilities, including a large deck, solar-heated pool and aromatherapy. ⊗ *Map M6 • 14 Derwent Rd • (021) 422 2763 • www.derwent house.co.za • RRRR*

4 Cape Grace

The aptly named Cape Grace offers stylish accommodation, a mind-boggling array of services, tasty Cape fusion cuisine and an informal but attentive management. Some rooms have a private balcony. ⊗ *Map Q2 • West Quay Rd, The V&A Waterfront • (021) 410 7100 • www.capegrace. com • RRRRR*

5 Victoria & Alfred Hotel

Converted from an old Victorian warehouse, this hotel rises from the heart of the V&A Waterfront, ensuring that all the airy rooms have good views. Loft suites come with a heavier price tag than standard rooms. ⊗ *Map R3 • Albert Quay • (021) 419 6677 • www.vahotel. co.za • RRRRR*

6 Western Grand Cape Town Arabella Quays

This state-of-the-art hotel is a tower looming over the Waterfront. Geared mainly towards business travellers, it has a rather characterless feel, but there's no quibbling with the five-star facilities. ⊗ *Map Q3 • 1 Lower Long St • (021) 412 9999 • www. starwoodhotels.com • RRRRR*

7 Waterfront Village

The all-suite accommodation of this five-star hotel has many amenities, making it suitable for families. ⊗ *Map Q2 • 4 West Quay Rd, The V&A Waterfront • (021) 421 5040 • www.waterfront village.com • RRRR*

8 The Grand Daddy Hotel

Without a doubt the most delightful feature of this creatively designed hotel is the penthouse trailer park on the roof. Featuring seven vintage Airstream caravans each uniquely decorated by local artists, such as the Goldilocks and the Three Bears caravan by Mark and Joe Stead. ⊗ *Map P5 • 38 Long Street • (021) 424 7247 • www. granddaddy.co.za • RRRR*

9 The Bay Hotel

This elegant hotel with its curvaceous exterior offers direct access to the popular Camps Bay beach. Well-equipped (as you would expect a five-star hotel to be), the hotel's upper-storey rooms offer stunning mountain views. ⊗ *Map H1 • 69 Victoria Rd, Camps Bay • (021) 438 4444 • www.thebay.co.za • RRRRR*

10 12 Apostles Hotel & Spa

On the Atlantic-facing slopes of Table Mountain and below the magnificent Twelve Apostles formation, this five-star boutique hotel has exceptional rooms, superb service and an outstanding spa. It also offers guided walks into the surrounding *fynbos*. ⊗ *Map H1 • Victoria Rd, Camps Bay • (021) 437 9000 • www.12apostles hotel.com • RRRRR*

Unless otherwise stated, all hotels accept credit cards, have en-suite bathrooms and air conditioning

Streetsmart

Left **Cape Town Hollow Boutique Hotel** Right **Cape Heritage Hotel room**

Mid-Range Hotels

1 Cape Town Hollow Boutique Hotel

This contemporary four-star hotel is within walking distance of plenty of restaurants, bars and nightspots. It has an Italian restaurant and a spa. ⊗ *Map P5 • 88 Queen Victoria St • (021) 423 1260 • www.capetown hollow.co.za • RRR*

2 Cape Heritage Hotel

This historic hotel overlooking Heritage Square has 15 individually decorated rooms with antique features such as 19th-century wood floors and high-beamed ceilings. South Africa's oldest vineyard is in the courtyard. ⊗ *Map Q4 • 90 Bree St • (021) 424 4646 • www. capeheritage.co.za • RRR*

3 Cape Diamond Hotel

Overlooking the Company's Garden, this attractive relic of the 1930s Art Deco movement is wonderfully central and offers good value. Its ground-floor restaurant opens onto the street. ⊗ *Map Q5 • Cnr Longmarket & Parliament St • (021) 461 2519 • Breakfast excl • www.cape diamondhotel.co.za • RR*

4 The Townhouse

This reasonably priced 106-room hotel has all modern conveniences. The spacious rooms have made extensive use of wood and earthy colours. ⊗ *Map Q5 • 60 Corporation Rd • (021) 465 7050 • Breakfast excl • www.townhouse.co.za • RRR*

5 Four Rosmead Boutique Guesthouse

Built in 1903, this hotel is a classified monument that has been stylishly remodelled. The interiors are subtle but have a distinctive African spirit enhanced by local art. Facilities include a pamper room and a patio overlooking a pool. ⊗ *Map N6 • 4 Rosmead Rd • (021) 480 3810 • www. fourrosmead.com • RRR*

6 Winchester Mansions Hotel

This 1920s building set around a bougainvillea-clad courtyard has a beachfront location at Sea Point. Rooms on the lower floor have a floral Edwardian feel while those on the upper floors are spacious and contemporary. ⊗ *Map L2 • 221 Beach Rd, Sea Pt • (021) 434 2351 • www. winchester.co.za • RRR*

7 Peninsula All-Suite Hotel

This seafront Art Deco high-rise hotel offers spectacular views and has self-catering apartments. Facilities include a pool, a sunset deck and also a complimentary shuttle to various sites. The surrounding area has many shops for self-caterers. Popular with families and small groups. ⊗ *Map I4 • 313 Beach Rd, Sea Pt • (021) 430 7777 • www. peninsula.co.za • RRRR*

8 Wilton Manor

Lying in a quiet corner of Green Point, minutes away from the city centre, this restored Victorian manor has a wraparound balcony, pressed ceilings and wooden floors. Its thatched wooden deck has a heated pool. The seven double rooms can be booked individually or as a unit. ⊗ *Map N2 • 15 Croxteth Rd, Green Pt • (021) 434 7869 • www. fullhouserentals.co.za • RR*

9 Cape Standard

Small and reasonably priced, this hotel combines modern European minimalism with subtle African touches to create a light, spacious feel and is within striking distance of the city centre. Its small, leafy garden has a plunge pool. ⊗ *Map M2 • 3 Romney St, Green Pt • (021) 430 3060 • www. capestandard.co.za • RRR*

10 Villa Rosa

Splendidly restored, this Victorian brick-faced mansion is a charming guesthouse. It is conveniently close to the city centre and the Waterfront. ⊗ *Map L4 • 277 High Level Rd, Sea Pt • (021) 434 2768 • www. villa-rosa.com • RR*

Left **Daddy Longlegs' "Doctor and Nurses" room** Centre **Extreme Hotel** Right **Tudor Hotel**

🔟 Budget Hotels

1 Daddy Longlegs
Situated at the heart of the action on Long Street, this bold boutique hotel defies conventional description. Each of its 12 rooms have been uniquely, if rather bizarrely, decorated by different artists. 🕙 *Map D4 • 134 Long St • (021) 422 3074 • www. daddylonglegs.co.za • RR*

2 Protea Hotel Fire and Ice
This offshoot of the Protea chain is aimed at the younger, hipper crowd, with its action-themed decor, state-of-the-art viewing room and designer burger bar with views into the glass-sided pool. Its 130 rooms are comfortable, but a touch cramped. 🕙 *Map N5 • 198 Bree St • (021) 488 2555 • www.extreme-hotels.com • RRR*

3 Tudor Hotel
This three-star hotel – the oldest in the city centre – has a sense of history complemented by an appealing, contemporary decor and good facilities. Each room is uniquely furnished. It is one of the best deals in central Cape Town. 🕙 *Map P4 • 153 Longmarket St • (021) 424 1335 • www. tudor hotel.co.za • RR*

4 Underberg Guesthouse
Built as a farmhouse in the 1860s, this charming 11-room guesthouse has a pretty setting below Table Mountain. Modern facilities include wireless connectivity. Its location is convenient to explore the city centre and the Waterfront. 🕙 *Map N5 • 6 Tamboerskloof Rd, Tamboerskloof • (021) 426 2262 • Breakfast excl • www.under bergguesthouse.co.za • RR*

5 Breakwater Lodge
Formerly a prison, this hotel, a stone's throw away from the Waterfront, retains an institutional feel. The rooms are comfortable and there's a good self-service canteen. 🕙 *Map P2 • Portswood Rd, The V&A Waterfront • (021) 406 1911 • Breakfast excl • www.bwl.co.za • RR*

6 Waterfront City Lodge
Part of the national City Lodge chain, this hotel is an affordable option within walking distance of the Waterfront. Room rates are on par with the Breakwater, but the location is less convenient. 🕙 *Map Q3 • Cnr Alfred & Dock Rds • (021) 419 9450 • Breakfast excl • www.citylodge. co.za • RRR*

7 Protea Hotel Cape Castle
A few steps away from the restaurants and shops of the V&A Waterfront, this all-suite hotel consists of 67 luxury apartments with fully equipped kitchens.

You can enjoy waterfront views from every apartment. 🕙 *Map P2 • 3 Main Rd, Green Point • (021) 439 1016 • Breakfast excl • www.proteahotels.com • RR*

8 De Waterkant Village
This street-long complex in the Bo-Kaap area has 80 self-catering units, from simple crash pads to the more expensive plush apartments. It is perfect for visits to the boutiques, restaurants and nightclubs of De Waterkant (the Water's Edge). 🕙 *Map P3 • Loader St, De Waterkant • (021) 409 2500 • www.dewater kant.com • RRR*

9 Don Suite Hotel
This all-suite chain hotel in Sea Point is separated from the ocean by green spaces. The self-catering apartments boast balconies offering sunset views over the Atlantic. 🕙 *Map K3 • 249 Beach Rd, Sea Pt • (021) 434 1083 • www. don.co.za • RR*

10 Road Lodge Airport
The only accommodation close to the international airport, this no-frills hotel is within walking distance of all terminals and offers cheap transfers to travellers with heavy luggage (see p104). 🕙 *Map C3 • Cape Town International Airport • (021) 934 7303 • www.citylodge.co.za • R*

Price Categories

For a standard, double room per night (breakfast not included), taxes and service charges.

R	under R500
RR	R500–1,000
RRR	R1,000–1,500
RRRR	R1,500–2,000
RRRRR	over R2,000

Steenberg Hotel

TOP 10 Southern Suburbs & Peninsula Hotels

1 Andros Boutique Hotel

One of the most exclusive addresses in Cape Town, this century-old Cape Dutch homestead was designed by Sir Herbert Baker. All eight rooms have verandas and antique furnishings. There is also a suite with a private pool. Facilities include a gym, beauty salon and a candlelit French restaurant. ✪ *Map H2 • Cnr Newlands & Phyllis, Claremont • (021) 797 9777 • www.andros. co.za • RRRRR*

2 Vineyard Hotel & Spa

Centred on a 200-year-old residence built for Lady Anne Barnard, this luxurious hotel offers a variety of accommo-dations, a quartet of restaurants that includes a sushi bar and two heated pools. ✪ *Map H2 • 60 Colinton Rd, Newlands • (021) 657 4500 • www. vineyard.co.za • RRRR*

3 Cellars-Hohenort

This gracious five-star hotel is set in grounds bordering Kirstenbosch National Botanical Garden. A classy set-up, it has a strong period feel and two excellent restaurants, of which the Cape Malay *(see p52)* offers delicious Cape cuisine. ✪ *Map H2 • 93 Brommersvlei Rd, Constantia • (021) 794 2137 • www.cellars-hohenort. com • RRRRR*

4 Constantia Uitsig

In the Constantia Winelands, this 16-room boutique hotel is built around a Cape Dutch farmhouse. Dine at the estate's three award-winning restaurants. ✪ *Map H2 • Spaanschemat River Rd, Constantia • (021) 794 6500 • www.uitsig. co.za • RRRRR*

5 The Constantia

This boutique hotel has five superior doubles, and two suites. The hotel operates as a B&B combining Cape country decor with a scattering of modern African art. The staff prepares meals on request or you can explore the dining options nearby. ✪ *Map H2 • Spaanschemat River Rd, Constantia • (021) 794 6561 • www.theconstantia.com • RRRRR*

6 Steenberg Hotel

This intimate five-star hotel on the Steenberg Estate boasts fine thatched and gabled Cape Dutch architecture. The acclaimed Catharina at Steenberg Restaurant is also here *(see p75)*. Guests can access the exclusive Steenberg Golf Course. ✪ *Map H2 • Cnr Steenberg & Tokai, Constantia • (021) 713 2222 • www.steenberg hotel. com • RRRRR*

7 Quayside Hotel

This wallet-friendly four-star hotel is wonderfully located in Quayside Centre. Its rooms are very large; it is worth paying the slight premium for a sea-facing one with a balcony. ✪ *Map H4 • Jubilee Sq, St George's St, Simon's Town • (021) 786 3838 • www. relaishotels.com • RRR*

8 British Hotel Apartments

Ideal for families, the big self-catering apartments in this Victorian manor have ornate balconies facing Simon's Town's waterfront. ✪ *Map H4 • St George's Rd, Simon's Town • (021) 786 2214 • www.britishhotelapart ments.co.za • RRR*

9 Lord Nelson Inn

This inn is the longest-serving hostelry on the Cape Peninsula. The homely accommo-dation is great value for money and the pub has plenty of character. If the food is not to your taste, there are many eateries nearby. ✪ *Map H4 • 58 George's St, Simon's Town • (021) 786 1386 • www. lordnelsoninn.co.za • RR*

10 Boulders Beach Lodge and Restaurant

In a beautiful location at the entrance to Boulders Coastal Park, this 14-room lodge (two self-catering) also has a restaurant serving Pacific Rim cuisine. ✪ *Map H4 • 4 Boulders Plc • (021) 786 1758 • www. bouldersbeach.co.za • RR*

→ *Recommend your favourite hotel on traveldk.com*

115

Left **Lobby of D'Ouwe Werf** Centre **Mont Rochelle** Right **Wild Mushroom Boutique Hotel**

🔟 Winelands Town Hotels

1 D'Ouwe Werf
Established in 1802 on the foundations of a fire-damaged church, this Stellenbosch institution is South Africa's oldest country inn. It has a handy location on historic Church Street. Atmospheric and affordable, it has well-equipped rooms and a fine Cape restaurant. ◈ *Map D2 • 30 Church St, Stellenbosch • (021) 887 4608 • www. ouwewerf.com • RRR*

2 Eendracht Hotel
An award-winning three-star hotel set in a restored 18th-century homestead. Most of its dozen rooms come with private balconies that overlook historic Dorp Street. There's also a salt-water pool and a coffee shop. ◈ *Map D2 • 161 Dorp St, Stellenbosch • (021) 883 8843 • www. eendracht-hotel.com • RRR*

3 Protea Hotel Dorpshuis & Spa
This homely four-star boutique hotel is housed at the quieter end of historic Dorp Street. Antique furnishings decorate the 28 rooms, and there's a pool in the shady garden. ◈ *Map D2 • 22 Dorp St, Stellenbosch • (021) 883 9881 • www. dorpshuis.co.za • RRR*

4 Batavia Boutique Hotel
This five-room hotel off Dorp Street aims to recreate the atmosphere of a Dutch East India Company (VOC) *(see p34)* lodge with its Oriental carpets, ostrich leather furniture and classical paintings. ◈ *Map D2 • 12 Louw St, Stellenbosch • (021) 887 2914 • www. bataviahouse.co.za • RRR*

5 Wild Mushroom Boutique Hotel
This luxurious boutique hotel has six suites each one themed to a different mushroom species in an imaginative and sophisticated way. There is also a delightful garden and a swimming pool. ◈ *Map D2 • 39 Digteby Estate, Vlottenburg Rd, Stellenbosch • (021) 886 9880 • www.wildmushroom.co.za • RRR*

6 Old Tulbagh Hotel
This small, family-run hotel stands in the historic heart of Tulbagh. Its spacious rooms have wooden floors and elegant furnishings. The attached Shamrock and Thistle is a friendly Celtic pub that is popular with tourists and locals. ◈ *Map H3 • 22 van der Stel Street, Tulbagh • (023) 230 0071 • www.tulbagh hotel.co.za • RR*

7 Le Quartier Français
Best known for its pair of acclaimed restaurants, The Tasting Room and iCi, this legendary hotel offers five-star accommodation. Its large, hardwood-furnished rooms are situated around a leafy courtyard and pool. ◈ *Map F2 • 16 Huguenot Rd, Franschhoek • (021) 876 2151 • www. lequartier.co.za • RRRRR*

8 Mont Rochelle
Resurrected from the ashes of the burnt-down Hotel Le Couronne, this five-star hotel on Mont Rochelle Wine Estate has wonderful views over Franschhoek. Built in the classic Cape Dutch style, it has elegant rooms and suites. It also has a wine-tasting centre. ◈ *Map F2 • Dassenberg Rd, Franschhoek • (021) 876 2770 • www.montrochelle.co.za • RRRRR*

9 Auberge La Dauphine
Set on the Auberge La Dauphine Wine Estate, this guesthouse offers a countrified setting. Its six rooms are all named after different grapes. It also offers carp fishing in a private dam. ◈ *Map F2 • Verdun Rd, Franschhoek • (021) 876 2606 • www.la dauphine.co.za • RR*

10 Grand Roche
One of the top hotels in the Winelands, Grande Roche on Paarl's outskirts is built around a lovely Cape Dutch manor now listed as a national monument. Its 34 plush suites come with wonderful views. ◈ *Map E1 • Plantasie St, Paarl • (021) 863 5100 • www.grande roche.co.za • RRRRR*

Stellenbosch Lodge

🔟 Winelands Rural Hotels

1 Devon Valley

This popular, four-star country retreat on Sylvanvale Estate offers lovely views and retains an Edwardian feel. Guided walks through surrounding vineyards are on offer. The hotel also boasts the award-winning Flavours Restaurant. 🅢 Map D2 • Devon Valley Rd, near Stellenbosch • (021) 865 2012 • www.devon valleyhotel.com • RRR

2 Lanzerac

Situated on the outskirts of Stellenbosch, this prestigious hotel is centred on a handsome 300-year-old Cape Dutch manor. Equipped with five-star facilities, the whole set-up positively exudes luxury. 🅢 Map E3 • Lanzerac Rd • (021) 886 5641 • www.lanzerac.co.za • RRRRR

3 Kleine Zalze Lodges

This lodge lies in an oak copse, a 10-minute drive away from Stellenbosch on Kleine Zalze Estate. Most of the comfortable rooms have self-catering facilities. Try some fine Provençal food at the Terroir Restaurant. 🅢 Map D3 • Technopak Rd (off R44), Stellenbosch • (021) 880 0740 • www.kleine zalze.co.za • RRR

4 Stellenbosch Lodge

This four-star hotel is on the Blaauwklippen Estate, which is to the south of Stellenbosch. Its 53 functional rooms are in a new Cape Dutch-styled thatch building. The hotel's restaurant specializes in traditional Cape cuisine. 🅢 Map D3 • Canterbury Rd, Blaauw-klippen • (021) 888 0100 • www.stblodge.co.za • RR

5 Spier Hotel

This mould-breaking four-star hotel overlooks the Eerste River on Spier Farm, a short drive from Stellenbosch. Its bold decor is an adventurous fusion of African themes and modern Pop Art. Well placed to explore other estates. 🅢 Map D3 • Spier Wine Farm • (021) 809 1100 • www.spier.co.za • RRRR

6 Zewenwacht Country Inn

This cosy hilltop inn lies on Zewenwacht Estate and offers accommo-dation in air conditioned suites with private ter-races; on a clear day, you can see as far as Table Bay. It has a clubhouse, pool, playground and an acclaimed restaurant. 🅢 Map C3 • Langerverwacht Rd, Stellenbosch • (021) 903 5123 • www.zeven wacht.co.za • RRR

7 Papyrus Lodge

Built around a picturesque lake below Helderberg Mountains, this lodge offers accom-modation in stilted wooden chalets jutting out over the water. The more landlocked, superior suites are in the Cape Dutch style. 🅢 Map D3 • Winery Rd, Near Stellenbosch • (021) 842 3606 • www.papyruslodge. co.za • RRR

8 Alluvia Guesthouse

Set on the eponymous boutique wine estate on Helshoogte Pass, this exclusive guesthouse consists of five stylishly decorated, self-catering cottages. Wine-tasting is only for the guesthouse residents. Other activities include fly-fishing and golf. 🅢 Map E2 • Helshoogte Pass • (021) 885 1661 • www.alluvia.co. za • RRRR

9 Eikendal Lodge

This vine-draped lodge is set among the Eikendal Estate vine-yards. There is a good restaurant and the facil-ities include a natural health centre. 🅢 Map D3 • R44 south of Stellenbosch • (021) 855 3617 • www. eikendal.com • RRR

10 Lekkerwijn Homestead

This gabled Cape Dutch homestead was built in the early 18th century in the Groot Drakenstein Valley. Classically decorat-ed rooms lie in shady gardens where peacocks and guineafowls parade around the pool. 🅢 Map E2 • Groot Drakenstein Valley • (021) 874 1122 • www.lekkerwijn.com • RR

Left **Kagga Kamma** Centre **Cliff Lodge** Right **Lambert's Bay Hotel**

ᵀᴼᴾ10 Hotels Beyond the Winelands

1 The Marine Hermanus

The top address in Hermanus offering accommodation in 42 rooms and suites. The patio is a natural vantage point for whale watching, and facilities include a spa, heated swimming pool, tidal pool, Internet lounge and two great restaurants. ⊗ *Map U5 • Marine Drive, Hermanus • (028) 313 1000 • RRRRR*

2 Misty Waves Boutique Hotel

This great set-up, a curvaceous double-storey building on the cliffs, has a cosy lounge, a kidney-shaped pool, rooftop Jacuzzi, good seafood and excellent whale watching from private verandas. ⊗ *Map U5 • 21 Marine Drive, Hermanus • (028) 313 8460 • www. hermanusmistybeach.co.za • RRRRR*

3 Abalone Guest House

Situated on Sievers Point, this homely and pleasantly decorated guesthouse is well located for cliff walks, whale watching and exploring the small town centre. ⊗ *Map U5 • 306 Main Rd, Hermanus • (044) 533 1345 • www.abalone lodge.co.za • RRR*

4 Cliff Lodge

This award-winning guesthouse with a magnificent clifftop location outside Gansbaai offers grand views. It consists of just four spacious rooms, a shared conservatory and deck with ocean views and a plunge pool. ⊗ *Map U6 • De Kelders, Gansbaai • (028) 384 0983 • www. clifflodge.co.za • RRR*

5 Agulhas Country Lodge

Set on a hill overlooking the southernmost point in Africa, this family-run guesthouse offers just eight rooms, all with great views, and some of the best seafood on the south coast. ⊗ *Map V6 • Main Rd, L'Agulhas • (028) 435 7650 • www.agulhas countrylodge.com • RRRR*

6 De Hoop Cottages and Lodges

A variety of Cape Dutch-style family cottages and smaller self-catering units are studded around this lovely reserve. It's all reasonably priced but be aware that there are no shops or restaurants, so bring your own provisions. ⊗ *Map W5 • De Hoop Nature Reserve • (021) 659 3500 • www. capenature.co.za • R*

7 Kagga Kamma Private Reserve

This luxurious lodge is noted for its wealth of prehistoric rock art. Guided safaris to the rock art sites also explore the local fauna and flora. Other facilities include a pool built into the rocks and a restaurant serving South African cuisine. ⊗ *Map U3 • Ceres • (021) 872 4343 • www. kaggakamma.co.za • RRR*

8 Protea Hotel Saldanha Bay

This unpretentious member of the Protea chain has a seafront location in Saldanha Bay. It's a good base for exploring the West Coast National Park and has a range of facilities. ⊗ *Map S3 • Sib, Saldanha Bay • (022) 714 1264 • Breakfast excl • www. proteahotels.com • RRR*

9 Farr Out B&B

This pleasant four-room B&B has a lovely location in Paternoster. Two of the rooms have balconies with sea views. It is a convenient place to enjoy the sights of Cape Columbine. ⊗ *Map S2 • 17 Seemeeusingel Paternoster • (022) 752 2222 • www.madein paternoster.co.za • RR*

10 Lambert's Bay Hotel

Attractively situated on Lambert's Bay's quaint fishing harbour, the rooms are pleasant. Rooms with sea-views are pricier. The restaurant is known for its seafood, best had with a West Coast wine. ⊗ *Map S1 • 72 Voortrekker Rd, Lambert's Bay • (027) 432 1126 • www.lamberts bayhotel.co.za • RR*

Price Categories

For a standard, double room per night (breakfast not included), taxes and services charges.

R	under R500
RR	R500–1,000
RRR	R1,000–1,500
RRRR	R1,500–2,000
RRRRR	over R2,000

Cat & Moose Backpackers

🔟 Backpacker Hostels

1 Long Street Backpackers

The oldest, and probably the best, backpacker hotel along Long Street, this is within easy reach of the trendy nightspots. It is a secure, friendly and lively place for those who want to be at the heart of the urban action. ◎ Map P5 • 209 Long St • (021) 423 0615 • Breakfast excl • www.longstreetbackpackers.co.za • R

2 Cat & Moose Backpackers

Another veteran of Long Street, this hostel is in a 200-year-old house with wooden floors and earthy African decor. It has a great location for partying, and is well set up for chilling out. ◎ Map Q4 • 305 Long St • (021) 423 7638 • Breakfast excl • www.catandmoose.co.za • R

3 Ashanti Lodge

A place that combines upmarket decor with a relaxed party atmosphere. Good, light meals and chilled drinks are served here. The wide deck has fantastic views of Table Mountain. ◎ Map P6 • 11 Hof St, Gardens • (021) 423 8721 • Breakfast excl • www.ashanti.co.za • R

4 The Backpack

One of South Africa's oldest backpacker hotel offers more luxurious accommodation along with the standard rooms and dorms. It has a vastly experienced travel centre for excursions. ◎ Map N5 • 74 New Church St, Tamboerskloof • (021) 423 4530 • Breakfast excl • www.backpackers.co.za • R

5 St John's Waterfront Lodge

Set in the inner city suburb of Green Point, this well-established and welcoming hostel is a short walk from the V&A Waterfront (not advisable late at night) and a bus ride from the city. ◎ Map P2 • 6 Braemar Rd, Green Pt • (021) 439 1404 • Breakfast excl • www.stjohns.co.za • R

6 Simon's Town Backpackers

This unpretentious hostel is suited more to those who enjoy the outdoors. Situated within walking distance of the Boulders penguin colony and Seaforth Beach, it is close to many eateries. ◎ Map H4 • 66 St George St • (021) 786 1964 • Breakfast excl • www.capepax.co.za • R

7 Stumble Inn

Stumble Inn is located close to historic Dorp Street, and thus convenient for exploring the city centre. Facilities include a pool and TV lounge. ◎ Map P2 • 12 Market St, Stellenbosch • (021) 887 4049 • Breakfast excl • www.jump.to/stumble • R

8 Otter's Bend

Filling a gap in Franschhoek's accommodation scene, this new budget hostel has a pretty location. Many outdoor activities can be arranged from here. Eating out is quite costly, but good, in Franschhoek. ◎ Map F2 • Dassenberg Rd, Franschhoek • (021) 876 3200 • Breakfast excl • www.ottersbendlodge.co.za • R

9 Hermanus Backpackers

This lively hostel in Hermanus has many types of accommodation and offers activities from caged shark dives at Gansbaai to cliff walks and wine tasting along the under-publicized Walker Bay wine route. ◎ Map U5 • 26 Flower St, Hermanus • (028) 312 4293 • www.hermanusbackpackers.co.za • R

10 The Beach Camp

The ultimate backpacker hostel for outdoor enthusiasts, this camp offers simple accommodation in tents and A-frames. Other attractions include sea kayaking, guided walks through the reserve, sandy beaches, coastal fynbos, spring wildflowers and fresh seafood. ◎ Map S2 • Cape Columbine Nature Reserve, Paternoster • (082) 926 2267 • Breakfast excl • www.ratrace.co.za • R

 Almost all backpacker hostels have dormitory accommodation for under R100 per person.

General Index

Acknowledgments

The Author
Born in Britain and raised in Johannesburg, Philip Briggs is the author of more than a dozen travel guides about Africa. He is also a regular contributor to magazines such as Travel Africa, Africa Geographic, Wanderlust and BBC Wildlife.

Photographer
Tony Souter

AT DORLING KINDERSLEY

Publisher
Douglas Amrine

List Manager
Christine Stroyan

Managing Art Editor
Mabel Chan

Senior Editor
Sadie Smith

Project Designers
Paul Jackson
Shahid Mahmood

Senior Cartographic Editor
Casper Morris

Senior Cartographic Designer Suresh Kumar

Cartographer
Zafar-ul-Islam Khan

DTP Operator
Natasha Lu

Production
Linda Dare

Fact Checker
Loren Minsky

Revisions
Emma Anacootee, Andrew Baranowski, Sam Merrell, Sonal Modha

Picture Credits

t=top; tc=top centre; tr=top right; cla=centre left above; ca=centre above; cra=centre right above; cl=centre left; c=centre; cr=centre right; clb=centre left below; cb=centre below; crb=centre right below; bl=bottom left; bc=bottom centre; br=bottom right.

The photographer, writers and publisher would like to thank the media staff at the following sights and organizations for their helpful cooperation:

AGULHAS COUNTRY LODGE: Melanie Cleary 99tl.

ALAMY: AfriPics.com 48tl; Fabrice Bettex 55tl; Danita Delimont 36b, 43tl; Danita Delimont/Cindy Miller Hopkins 92–3; David Sanger Photography 1c; Martin Harvey 12b; Kari Herbert 89tl; Fried von Horsten 40b; Pierre Logwin 34b; Eric Nathan 88tl; Bernard O'Kane 54t; Pictures Colour Library 6ca; Frances Roberts 35tl; Grant Rooney 54br; Steve Allen Travel Photography 18–19c; Peter Titmuss 7bl, 12cla.

ANNETTE ASHLEY & ASSOCIATES: 68tl.

Courtesy of CLIFF LODGE: 118tc.

CORBIS: Franz-Marc Frei 56–7; Gallo Images/ Paul Velasco 34tl; John Hicks 28–9c; Hoberman Collection 12–13c; Hulton-Deutsch Collection 34tr; Mark A. Johnson 32–3; Henrik Trygg 49t.

EPA: Nic Bothma 3br, 46br, 48br.

IMAGES OF AFRICA: Shaen Adey 40tr, 94cr; Nigel Dennis 97tl; Hein von Horsten 83tr; Lanz von Horsten 3tr, 76tr, 94t; Walter Knirr 77tl, 94cl; Peter Pickford 40c.

Courtesy of KAGGA KAMMA PRIVATE GAME RESERVE: 118tl.

Courtesy of LAMBERT'S BAY HOTEL: 118tr.

RABBIT IN A HAT PR: 112tr.

REUTERS: Howard Burditt 46tc.

VISAGE MEDIA SERVICES: Getty Images/ Frans Lemmens 24–5c.

IAN WEBB: 49br.

Selected Street and Towns Index